POEMS OF
GEORGE GORDON,
LORD BYRON

POEMS OF
GEORGE GORDON,
LORD BYRON

Selected by Horace Gregory
Drawings by Virgil Burnett

THOMAS Y. CROWELL COMPANY
NEW YORK

THE CROWELL POETS
Under the editorship of Lillian Morrison

CONTENTS

INTRODUCTION

During the brief span of years through which he lived, particularly the interval from 1816 to his death at the age of thirty-six in 1824, George Gordon, Lord Byron's name was as widely known in Europe as it was fuel for gossip in his native London. He was almost as notorious as Lord Nelson and Napoleon Bonaparte. He set new styles in dress: the open collar and the loosely knotted scarf grew famous because he wore them. According to Peter Quennell's *Byron: The Years of Fame,* no Victorian household could call itself complete without a Turkey carpet and an aspidistra plant in the front parlor. These furnishings were, of course, the belated results of reading Byron's tales in verse, with their Oriental trappings and Balkan scenery.

For a generation after his death, fashions in sentimental American verse followed his lead, and strains of his drawing-room lyricism could, at times, be overheard in the writings of Edgar Allan Poe. Poe's admiration for "Though the day of my destiny's over" was typical of many American responses to Byronic sentiment.

Byronic fashions had behind them an irresistible force, a legend of love-making, of sin, of guilt, which strongly resembled the atmosphere and plot of Mozart's *Don Giovanni*. Therefore, it was appropriate that Byron's semi-autobiography in verse should be entitled *Don Juan*. Byron, too, had made conquests of many women. His image was that of the Demon Lover who was also the Doomed Hero, and since in his travels he seemed both to ride the clouds above the map of Europe and to pace the earth, his legend held within it the Faustian aspect of Don Juan. No wonder Goethe at Weimar, with his own *Faust* in mind, was so strongly attracted by rumours of the young English poet's adventures! In England, Byron's separation from his wife caused as great a stir as Napoleon's divorce from the Empress Josephine. His flight from England to resume his earlier wanderings across the Continent was in open defiance of British middle-class morality.

Yet Byron's position was not quite that of the poet poised against the conventions of society—it was that of one who because of his wealth, his inherited title, his clearly cut profile, and hyacinthine hair as well as a gift for writing poetry, placed him above rules that had been made for ordinary men. His stance was complicated by a Calvinistic sense of sin that had been instilled during his boyhood by an imaginative, strong-minded Scottish governess, and through his mother he shared a turbulent measure of Scottish blood. In *Don Juan* (Canto X, stanzas xvii-xviii) he confessed,

> But I am half a Scot by birth, and bred
> A whole one, and my heart flies to my head,
>
> As 'Auld Lang Syne' brings Scotland, one and all,
>   Scotch plaids, Scotch snoods, the blue hills and clear streams,
> The Dee, the Don, Balgounie's brig's *black wall,*
>   All my boy feelings, all my gentler dreams
> Of what I *then dreamt,* clothed in their own pall,
>   Like Banquo's offspring:—floating past me seems
> My childhood in this childishness of mine:
> I care not—'tis a glimpse of *'Auld Lang Syne.'*

His birth was also attended by superstitious awe, for he was born with a caul and a clubbed right foot, and through his courage he surmounted his handicap by a show of exaggerated masculinity. His career at Harrow and at Trinity College, Cambridge, was that of a well-to-do young man whose friends were few and whose studies seemed to be the least of his concerns. In male company he assumed the manners of a Regency buck and boasted of his skill in swimming.

As Lord Byron, he visited his seat in the House of Lords and quickly left it empty. Politics for the sake of politics bored him: though some of his friends were Whigs, though he joined them in his ridicule of the reigning house of Hanover and the Tories, in political company he chose to be known as the poet—the poet who defied all tyrannies. During the last few months of his life his energy was spent in fighting the Greek war of liberation from the Turks. He anticipated his last move by writing, "When a man hath no freedom to fight for at home . . ." (see page 28).

In poetry his tastes were far more conservative. Byron the poet remained half concealed behind the schoolboy at Harrow and the rakish undergraduate at Trinity. He was the author of two brilliantly precocious books of verse. The writing seemed extraordinarily facile and transparent. Byron's models were clear enough: his catchy, tuneful lyrics stemmed from Thomas Moore's melodies, his heroic couplets and his turns of satire from Alexander Pope and a once popular but now forgotten poet, William Gifford.

At twenty-five he had outgrown his earlier writings, his *Hours of Idleness,* his *English Bards and Scotch Reviewers.* By this time he had made his grand tour through the Mediterranean to Turkey and Greece, had published the first two cantos of *Childe Harold's Pilgrimage,* and waked "one morning in London to find himself famous." The melancholy, wandering Childe Harold was the ideal and handsome image of his author, and overnight Byron had become the hero of fashionable salons and drawing rooms. Among the young women who were not too shy to make advances was the vivacious, extremely pretty Lady Caroline Lamb, wife of Lord Melbourne. She reported that Byron was "mad, bad, and dangerous to know," a warning that did not diminish his popularity.

With the breakup of his marriage to Anne Isabella Milbanke (who had hoped to reform, or at least, domesticate him), he escaped to the Continent, traveling eastward through northern Italy to the Balkan peninsula of Greece. In Venice he discovered the Countess Teresa Guiccioli who traveled with him, indulged him, and, though married securely to an Italian nobleman, almost succeeded in making Byron (where his wife had failed) a faithful husband—yet he eluded her by marching off to Greece, to die a victim of uremia, near the battlefield of Missolonghi.

II

What of the Byron we are always happy to admire and to rediscover for ourselves? Today we have the advantage of a hindsight that many of his earlier readers lacked. The sometimes flashing, sometimes grandiloquent rhetoric of Childe Harold which enchanted his contemporaries no longer dazzles us. His hero's journey through Europe had been anticipated by others, for Byron's friends Thomas Campbell and Samuel Rogers, the banker-poet who held literary salons at his breakfast table, took pleasure in writing travelogues in verse. On the authority of a fashionable poet of the day, a Dr. Beattie, Byron chose the Spenserian stanza in which to recite his recent travels—and to this he added the manner of Ariosto's and James Thomson's descriptive sketches. On his grand tour of the Continent he was scarcely more than another sentimental traveler, another man of feeling who loved to rest his thoughts (and a weary elbow) upon a mass of historic ruins. What was new in the figure of Childe Harold was its resemblance to its easily bored and restless author.

Even before he published the last canto of Childe Harold, he grew critical of the very rhetoric that does not charm us today. He believed that poets like himself and Shelley and Keats had taken a wrong turning. To his publisher, John Murray, he wrote a tribute to Alexander Pope: "I am the more confirmed in this by having lately gone over some of our classics, particularly *Pope* . . . and I was really astonished . . . at the ineffable distance in point of sense, harmony, effect, and even *Imagination,* passion, and *Invention,* between the little Queen Anne's man, and us of the Lower Empire."

Meanwhile, the romances in verse of Sir Walter Scott had created a precedent for Byron's Near Eastern tales, "The Giaour," "The Bride of Abydos," and "The Corsair"—these were entertainments for the readers of their day. Byron's true genius—and art—in writing verse was of slower development than his great facility in turning out swiftly paced narrations, smoothly flowing effusions in lyric forms as well as melancholy, brooding closet dramas. The tragic Byron of *Manfred* was a sadly overweighted writer; as with other writers of his day, including Shelley, Byron's effort to emulate Shakespearean dramatic verse was fatal. The living, the apparently immortal Byron is elsewhere. One has early flashes of him among his "Occasional Pieces" retrieved from letters to his friends, from briskly measured passages in his *English Bards and Scottish Reviewers.* He had more than talent for writing satire and a positive genius for writing inextinguishable light verse. In Venice in 1817 he read John Hookham Frere's "Whistlecraft," a satire in imitation of the Italian Luigi Pulci's *ottava rima.* Frere's plea was for the use of conversational diction in writing poetry, and the Byron who had written so many engaging, free-mannered letters to

John Murray, his publisher, and to Thomas Moore, the Irish poet, promptly adapted Frere's suggestion and the *ottava rima* to his own use. His genius was at full stature. A month later he had completed *Beppo,* a mock romance, and it was also an oblique satire on his own romantic gestures. It was as though he had suddenly liberated himself from all moral cant as well as the closely entwining English vice of hypocrisy. He was now prepared to write his masterpiece in the rollicking eight-line stanzas of *Beppo* and to begin the progress of his *Don Juan.*

At last Byron had found his voice, and when Murray quoted a critic who suggested that the poet spend six or eight years composing a poem worthy of himself, he replied: "I hate tasks. And then 'seven or eight years!' God send us all well this day three months, let alone years . . . . is *Childe Harold* nothing? You have so many *'divine'* poems, is it nothing to have written a *Human* one? . . . Since you want *length,* you shall have enough of *Juan,* for I'll make 50 cantos."

With the dedicatory stanzas of *Don Juan* Byron set the tone for the greatest achievement in the writing of satire since the days of Dean Swift and Alexander Pope. His targets were the Lake Poets who when young had expressed pro-French Revolution sentiments, but who now accepted patronage from Tory sources in the British government. The once radical poets of the day were now rediscovered as deeply entrenched conservatives, including the poet laureate Robert Southey. Compared to theirs, Byron's position as that of a near-Whig resembles the place of Liberals today:

Bob Southey! You're a poet—Poet-laureate,
    And representative of all the race;
Although 'tis true that you turn'd out a Tory at
    Last,—yours has lately been a common case;
And now, my Epic Renegade! what are ye at?
    With all the Lakers, in and out of place?
A nest of tuneful persons, to my eye
Like 'four and twenty Blackbirds in a pye;

'Which pye being open'd they began to sing'
    (This old song and new simile holds good)
'A dainty dish to set before the King,'
    Or Regent, who admires such kind of food;—
And Coleridge, too, has lately taken wing,
    But like a hawk encumber'd with his hood,—
Explaining metaphysics to the nation—
I wish he would explain his Explanation.

However much or little we may be attracted by Byron's legend, it is good to overhear his voice in *Don
Juan*. And one must return to his letters as well as his
verse to share the excitement and enjoy the wit that attended his brief, courageous journey through the world.

In making my selection of Byron's writings, I have
attempted, as best as I could, to give the reader the es-
sential Byron.

My choices include a number of "Occasional Pieces,"
pointing the way toward *Don Juan*. My quotations from
Childe Harold have been less extensive for reasons which
I think have been made clear. Though *Beppo* was completed before Byron wrote the opening cantos of *Don
Juan*, I have placed it at the very end, so the reader may
enjoy at uninterrupted leisure a mock plot within a
lively span of *ottava rimas*.

This meant that my choices would have to include a few of his letters—for in the entire range of English and American poets, he was one of the best as well as the most entertaining of letter writers. One might almost say that in his letters as well as in most of his verse, he constantly refashioned and improved upon the facts of his adventurous life. At his best, he endowed the merest incident with the color and motion of enlightened wit. In one of his letters to John Murray he described a young Italian matron, a certain Margarita who was more than willing to please rich Englishmen. She was a quick-witted, domineering, and furious beauty whose story told by other lips than his might well have dropped into sordidness. Today his Margarita is as fiery and as volatile as when Byron met her in 1817.

In more respects than one, the Byron of the letters and of *Don Juan* seems to be a singularly modern poet. He, too, saw our civilization disrupted by great wars, the Napoleonic wars of conquest that swung back and forth across the map of Europe, and if his critical spirit has an affinity with the temper of our times, it is because his self-imposed exile gave him a view of the world that was not unlike our own. In this sense he resembled the American expatriates who discovered London and Paris shortly before and after World War I. There should be no claim that he influenced any of them, yet like them, he had learned to feel at home away from home, and like them, he refreshed the language of poetry by inventing a language of his own, one that resembled the conversation of his day, and is as much alive to us as when he wrote it.

OCCASIONAL PIECES

STANZAS WRITTEN IN PASSING THE AMBRACIAN GULF

Through cloudless skies, in silvery sheen,
  Full beams the moon on Actium's coast:
And on these waves, for Egypt's queen,
  The ancient world was won and lost.

And now upon the scene I look,
  The azure grave of many a Roman;
Where stern Ambition once forsook
  His wavering crown to follow woman.

Florence! whom I will love as well
  As ever yet was said or sung
(Since Orpheus sang his spouse from hell),
  Whilst thou art fair and I am young;

Sweet Florence! those were pleasant times,
  When worlds were staked for ladies' eyes:
Had bards as many realms as rhymes,
  Thy charms might raise new Antonies.

Though Fate forbids such things to be,
  Yet, by thine eyes and ringlets curl'd!
I cannot lose a world for thee,
  But would not lose thee for a world.

WRITTEN AFTER SWIMMING FROM SESTOS TO ABYDOS

If, in the month of dark December,
　　Leander, who was nightly wont
(What maid will not the tale remember?)
　　To cross thy stream, broad Hellespont!

If, when the wintry tempest roar'd,
　　He sped to Hero, nothing loth,
And thus of old thy current pour'd,
　　Fair Venus! how I pity both!

For *me*, degenerate modern wretch,
　　Though in the genial month of May,
My dripping limbs I faintly stretch,
　　And think I've done a feat to-day.

But since he cross'd the rapid tide,
　　According to the doubtful story,
To woo,—and—Lord knows what beside,
　　And swam for Love, as I for Glory;

'Twere hard to say who fared the best:
　　Sad mortals! thus the gods still plague you!
He lost his labour, I my jest;
　　For he was drown'd, and I've the ague.

MAID OF ATHENS, ERE WE PART

Ζωη μου, σας αγαπω.

Maid of Athens, ere we part,
Give, oh give me back my heart!
Or, since that has left my breast,
Keep it now, and take the rest!
Hear my vow, before I go,
Ζωη μου, σας αγαπω.

By those tresses unconfined,
Woo'd by each Ægean wind;
By those lids whose jetty fringe
Kiss thy soft cheeks' blooming tinge;
By those wild eyes like the roe,
Ζωη μου, σας αγαπω.

By that lip I long to taste;
By that zone-encircled waist;
By all the token-flowers that tell
What words can never speak so well;
By love's alternate joy and woe,
Ζωη μου, σας αγαπω.

Maid of Athens! I am gone:
Think of me, sweet! when alone.
Though I fly to Istambol,
Athens holds my heart and soul:
Can I cease to love thee? No!
Ζωη μου, σας αγαπω.

SHE WALKS IN BEAUTY

She walks in beauty, like the night
　　Of cloudless climes and starry skies;
And all that's best of dark and bright
　　Meet in her aspect and her eyes:
Thus mellow'd to that tender light
　　Which heaven to gaudy day denies.

One shade the more, one ray the less,
　　Had half impair'd the nameless grace
Which waves in every raven tress,
　　Or softly lightens o'er her face;
Where thoughts serenely sweet express
　　How pure, how dear their dwelling-place.

And on that cheek, and o'er that brow,
　　So soft, so calm, yet eloquent,
The smiles that win, the tints that glow,
　　But tell of days in goodness spent,
A mind at peace with all below,
　　A heart whose love is innocent!

VISION OF BELSHAZZAR

The King was on his throne,
　　The Satraps throng'd the hall:
A thousand bright lamps shone
　　O'er that high festival.
A thousand cups of gold,
　　In Judah deem'd divine—
Jehovah's vessels hold
　　The godless Heathen's wine!

In that same hour and hall,
　　The fingers of a hand
Came forth against the wall,
　　And wrote as if on sand:
The fingers of a man;—
　　A solitary hand
Along the letters ran,
　　And traced them like a wand.

The monarch saw, and shook,
　　And bade no more rejoice;
All bloodless wax'd his look,
　　And tremulous his voice.
'Let the men of lore appear,
　　The wisest of the earth,
And expound the words of fear,
　　Which mar our royal mirth.'

Chaldea's seers are good,
　　But here they have no skill;

And the unknown letters stood
   Untold and awful still.
   And Babel's men of age
   Are wise and deep in lore;
But now they were not sage,
   They saw—but knew no more.

A captive in the land,
   A stranger and a youth,
He heard the king's command,
   He saw that writing's truth,
The lamps around were bright.
   The prophecy in view;
He read it on that night,—
   The morrow proved it true.

'Belshazzar's grave is made,
   His kingdom pass'd away,
He, in the balance weigh'd,
   Is light and worthless clay;
The shroud his robe of state,
   His canopy the stone;
The Mede is at his gate!
   The Persian on his throne!'

THE DESTRUCTION OF SENNACHERIB

The Assyrian came down like the wolf on the fold,
And his cohorts were gleaming in purple and gold;
And the sheen of their spears was like stars on the sea,
When the blue wave rolls nightly on deep Galilee.

Like the leaves of the forest when Summer is green,
That host with their banners at sunset were seen:
Like the leaves of the forest when Autumn hath blown,
That host on the morrow lay wither'd and strown.

For the Angel of Death spread his wings on the blast,
And breathed in the face of the foe as he pass'd;
And the eyes of the sleepers wax'd deadly and chill,
And their hearts but once heaved, and for ever grew still!

And there lay the steed with his nostril all wide,
But through it there roll'd not the breath of his pride;
And the foam of his gasping lay white on the turf,
And cold as the spray of the rock-beating surf.

And there lay the rider distorted and pale,
And the dew on his brow, and the rust on his mail:
And the tents were all silent, the banners alone,
The lances unlifted, the trumpet unblown.

And the widows of Ashur are loud in their wail,
And the idols are broke in the temple of Baal;
And the might of the Gentile, unsmote by the sword,
Hath melted like snow in the glance of the Lord!

STANZAS FOR MUSIC

There be none of Beauty's daughters
    With a magic like thee;
And like music on the waters
    Is thy sweet voice to me:
When, as if its sound were causing
The charmed ocean's pausing,
The waves lie still and gleaming
And the lull'd winds seem dreaming:

And the midnight moon is weaving
    Her bright chain o'er the deep;
Whose breast is gently heaving,
    As an infant's asleep:
So the spirit bows before thee,
To listen and adore thee;
With a full but soft emotion,
Like the swell of Summer's ocean.

STANZAS TO AUGUSTA

Though the day of my destiny's over,
  And the star of my fate hath declined,
Thy soft heart refused to discover
  The faults which so many could find;
Though thy soul with my grief was acquainted,
  It shrunk not to share it with me,
And the love which my spirit hath painted
  It never hath found but in *thee*.

Then when nature around me is smiling,
  The last smile which answers to mine,
I do not believe it beguiling,
  Because it reminds me of thine;
And when winds are at war with the ocean,
  As the breasts I believed in with me,
If their billows excite an emotion,
  It is that they bear me from *thee*.

Though the rock of my last hope is shiver'd,
  And its fragments are sunk in the wave,
Though I feel that my soul is deliver'd
  To pain—it shall not be its slave.
There is many a pang to pursue me:
  They may crush, but they shall not contemn;
They may torture, but shall not subdue me;
  'Tis of *thee* that I think—not of them.

Though human, thou didst not deceive me,
  Though woman, thou didst not forsake,

Though loved, thou forborest to grieve me,
  Though slander'd, thou never couldst shake;
Though trusted, thou didst not disclaim me,
  Though parted, it was not to fly,
Though watchful, 'twas not to defame me,
  Nor, mute, that the world might belie.

Yet I blame not the world, nor despise it,
  Nor the war of the many with one;
If my soul was not fitted to prize it,
  'Twas folly not sooner to shun:
And if dearly that error hath cost me,
  And more than I once could foresee,
I have found that, whatever it lost me,
  It could not deprive me of *thee*.

From the wreck of the past, which hath perish'd,
  Thus much I at least may recall,
It hath taught me that what I most cherish'd
  Deserved to be dearest of all:
In the desert a fountain is springing,
  In the wide waste there still is a tree,
And a bird in the solitude singing,
  Which speaks to my spirit of *thee*.

TO THOMAS MOORE

My boat is on the shore,
   And my bark is on the sea;
But, before I go, Tom Moore,
   Here's a double health to thee!

Here's a sigh to those who love me,
   And a smile to those who hate;
And, whatever sky's above me,
   Here's a heart for every fate.

Though the ocean roar around me,
   Yet it still shall bear me on;
Though a desert should surround me,
   It hath springs that may be won.

Were't the last drop in the well,
   As I gasp'd upon the brink,
Ere my fainting spirit fell,
   'Tis to thee that I would drink.

With that water, as this wine,
   The libation I would pour
Should be—peace with thine and mine,
   And a health to thee, Tom Moore.

STANZAS

Could Love for ever
Run like a river,
And Time's endeavour
    Be tried in vain—
No other pleasure
With this could measure;
And like a treasure
    We'd hug the chain.

But since our sighing
Ends not in dying,
And, form'd for flying,
    Love plumes his wing;
Then for this reason
Let's love a season;
But let that season be only Spring.

When lovers parted
Feel broken-hearted,
And, all hopes thwarted,
    Expect to die;
A few years older,
Ah! how much colder
They might behold her
    For whom they sigh!
When link'd together,
In every weather,
They pluck Love's feather
    From out his wing—

He'll stay for ever,
But sadly shiver
Without his plumage, when past the Spring.

Like chiefs of Faction,
His life is action—
A formal paction
    That curbs his reign,
Obscures his glory,
Despot no more, he
Such territory
    Quits with disdain.
Still, still advancing,
With banners glancing,
His power enhancing,
    He must move on—
Repose but cloys him,
Retreat destroys him,
Love brooks not a degraded throne.

Wait not, fond lover!
Till years are over,
And then recover
    As from a dream.
While each bewailing
The other's failing,
With wrath and railing,
    All hideous seem—
While first decreasing,
Yet not quite ceasing,
Wait not till teasing

All passion blight:
If once diminish'd,
Love's reign is finish'd—
Then part in friendship—and bid goodnight.

So shall Affection
To recollection
The dear connexion
　　Bring back with joy:
You had not waited
Till, tired or hated,
Your passions sated
　　Began to cloy.

Your last embraces
Leave no cold traces—
The same fond faces
　　As through the past:
And eyes, the mirrors
Of your sweet errors,
Reflect but rapture—not least though last.

True, separations
Ask more than patience;
What desperations
　　From such have risen!
But yet remaining,
What is't but chaining
Hearts which, once waning,
　　Beat 'gainst their prison?
Time can but cloy love

And use destroy love:
The winged boy, Love,
   Is but for boys—
You'll find it torture,
Though sharper, shorter,
To wean, and not wear out your joys.

STANZAS

When a man hath no freedom to fight for at home,
   Let him combat for that of his neighbours;
Let him think of the glories of Greece and of Rome,
   And get knock'd on the head for his labours.

To do good to mankind is the chivalrous plan,
   And is always as nobly requited;
Then battle for freedom wherever you can,
   And, if not shot or hang'd, you'll get knighted.

STANZAS WRITTEN ON THE ROAD
BETWEEN FLORENCE AND PISA

Oh, talk not to me of a name great in story;
The days of our youth are the days of our glory;
And the myrtle and ivy of sweet two-and-twenty
Are worth all your laurels, though ever so plenty.

What are garlands and crowns to the brow that is wrin-
    kled?
'Tis but as a dead flower with May-dew besprinkied.
Then away with all such from the head that is hoary!
What care I for the wreaths that can *only* give glory!

Oh FAME!—if I e'er took delight in thy praises,
'Twas less for the sake of thy high-sounding phrases,
Than to see the bright eyes of the dear one discover,
She thought that I was not unworthy to love her.

There chiefly I sought thee, *there* only I found thee;
Her glance was the best of the rays that surround thee;
When it sparkled o'er aught that was bright in my story,
I knew it was love, and I felt it was glory.

SO WE'LL GO NO MORE A ROVING

So we'll go no more a roving
   So late into the night
Though the heart be still as loving,
   And the moon be still as bright.

For the sword outwears its sheath,
   And the soul wears out the breast,
And the heart must pause to breathe,
   And Love itself have rest.

Though the night was made for loving,
   And the day returns too soon,
Yet we'll go no more a roving
   By the light of the moon.

From
CHILDE HAROLD'S PILGRIMAGE

Fashionable and influential as *Childe Harold* was in Byron's day, the poem has become irrevocably dated. Byron's use of the Spenserean stanza for his travelogue was unfortunate. It helped to make the poem sound far more portentous and solemn than it had a right to be, for after all, Byron on his grand tour enjoyed himself in the same spirit that he wrote of his travels to his mother. The delicate architecture and music of the stanza did not lend themselves to the restless moods of Byron's temperament. Both Keats and Shelley employed the stanza with appropriate sensitivity and art. Only as a tour de force was the poem successful. For the time being Byron as Childe Harold (the archaic spelling of "Childe" and its associations with ancient balladry and baronial rule were suggested by reading Sir Walter Scott's notes on antiquities) became the best known of literary liberals. In the newly formed United States his influence and popularity were made secure by his high praise of George Washington and American independence. The Italy that Childe Harold saw was, of course, the Italy of a hundred and fifty years ago. I have selected four stanzas on Rome from Canto IV which seem less tarnished by time than other famous passages in the poem. The quotations in the opening lines of the third stanza are from Gibbon's classic history, *Decline and Fall of the Roman Empire*. To these I have added the often quoted eight stanzas from Canto III which contain Childe Harold's reflections on Waterloo. Those who have read Thackeray's *Vanity Fair* will have still another view of the battlefield Childe Harold saw.

ON ROME

A ruin—yet what ruin! from its mass
Walls, palaces, half-cities, have been rear'd;
Yet oft the enormous skeleton ye pass,
And marvel where the spoil could have appear'd.
Hath it indeed been plunder'd, or but clear'd?
Alas! developed, opens the decay,
When the colossal fabric's form is near'd:
It will not bear the brightness of the day,
Which streams too much on all—years—man—have reft
    away.

But when the rising moon begins to climb
Its topmost arch, and gently pauses there;
When the stars twinkle through the loops of time,
And the low night-breeze waves along the air
The garland-forest, which the gray walls wear,
Like laurels on the bald first Cæsar's head;
When the light shines serene but doth not glare,
Then in this magic circle raise the dead:
Heroes have trod this spot—'tis on their dust ye tread.

'While stands the Coliseum, Rome shall stand;
'When falls the Coliseum, Rome shall fall;
'And when Rome falls—the World.'
    From our own land
Thus spake the pilgrims o'er this mighty wall
In Saxon times, which we are wont to call
Ancient; and these three mortal things are still

On their foundations, and unalter'd all;
Rome and her Ruin past Redemption's skill,
The World, the same wide den—of thieves, or what ye
    will.

Simple, erect, severe, austere, sublime—
Shrine of all saints and temple of all gods,
From Jove to Jesus—spared and blest by time;
Looking tranquillity, while falls or nods
Arch, empire, each thing round thee, and man plods
His way through thorns to ashes—glorious dome!
Shalt thou not last? Time's scythe and tyrants' rods
Shiver upon thee—sanctuary and home
Of art and piety—Pantheon!—pride of Rome!

From Childe Harold's Pilgrimage, Canto IV

WATERLOO

There was a sound of revelry by night,
And Belgium's capital had gather'd then
Her Beauty and her Chivalry, and bright
The lamps shone o'er fair women and brave men;
A thousand hearts beat happily; and when
Music arose with its voluptuous swell,
Soft eyes look'd love to eyes which spake again,
And all went merry as a marriage bell;
But hush! hark! a deep sound strikes like a rising knell!

Did ye not hear it?—No; 'twas but the wind,
Or the car rattling o'er the stony street;
On with the dance! let joy be unconfined;
No sleep till morn, when Youth and Pleasure meet
To chase the glowing Hours with flying feet—
But hark!—that heavy sound breaks in once more,
As if the clouds its echo would repeat;
And nearer, clearer, deadlier than before!
Arm! Arm! it is—it is—the cannon's opening roar!

Within a window'd niche of that high hall
Sate Brunswick's fated chieftain; he did hear
That sound the first amidst the festival,
And caught its tone with Death's prophetic ear;
And when they smiled because he deem'd it near,
His heart more truly knew that peal too well
Which stretch'd his father on a bloody bier,
And roused the vengeance blood alone could quell;
He rush'd into the field, and, foremost fighting, fell.

Ah! then and there was hurrying to and fro,
And gathering tears, and tremblings of distress,
And cheeks all pale, which but an hour ago
Blush'd at the praise of their own loveliness;
And there were sudden partings, such as press
The life from out young hearts, and choking sighs
Which ne'er might be repeated; who could guess
If ever more should meet those mutual eyes,
Since upon night so sweet such awful morn could rise!

And there was mounting in hot haste: the steed,
The mustering squadron, and the clattering car,
Went pouring forward with impetuous speed,
And swiftly forming in the ranks of war;
And the deep thunder peal on peal afar;
And near, the beat of the alarming drum
Roused up the soldier ere the morning star;
While throng'd the citizens with terror dumb,
Or whispering, with white lips—'The foe! they come!
    they come!'

And wild and high the 'Cameron's gathering' rose!
The war-note of Lochiel, which Albyn's hills
Have heard, and heard, too, have her Saxon foes:—
How in the noon of night that pibroch thrills,
Savage and shrill! But with the breath which fills
Their mountain-pipe, so fill the mountaineers
With the fierce native daring which instils
The stirring memory of a thousand years,
And Evan's, Donald's fame rings in each clansman's ears!

And Ardennes waves above them her green leaves,
Dewy with nature's tear-drops as they pass,
Grieving, if aught inanimate e'er grieves,
Over the unreturning brave,—alas!
Ere evening to be trodden like the grass
Which now beneath them, but above shall grow
In its next verdure, when this fiery mass
Of living valour, rolling on the foe
And burning with high hope shall moulder cold and low.

Last noon beheld them full of lusty life,
Last eve in Beauty's circle proudly gay,
The midnight brought the signal-sound of strife,
The morn the marshalling in arms,—the day
Battle's magnificently stern array!
The thunder-clouds close o'er it, which when rent
The earth is cover'd thick with other clay,
Which her own clay shall cover, heap'd and pent,
Rider and horse,—friend, foe,—in one red burial blent!

From *Childe Harold's Pilgrimage,* Canto III

From
DON JUAN

Since *Don Juan* remained unfinished at Byron's death in 1824, it may be regarded as his last will and testament. The many-cantoed poem was an overflowing of the Byronic spirit, and reread today, its energy and wit seem tireless. In the following selections from it, I have attempted to convey something of the poem's shifting variety and enchantments: the first is a stanza written on the back of the manuscript of Canto I; the second is a passage from Canto II, from the love story of the pirate's daughter, Haidée, and Don Juan—which was the *beau ideal* of Byronic love; the third, from Canto III, is Byron's famous apostrophe to Greece; and the fourth is the opening passage from Canto XII which shows Byron as among the first of English poets to reveal the modern complex of wills to power, of gold and money-making, of politics and wars, of high finance and banking. And this recognition of forces in the world around him was also a sign of his approaching middle age.

FRAGMENT

On the Back of the Poet's MS. of Canto I

I would to heaven that I were so much clay,
    As I am blood, bone, marrow, passion, feeling—
Because at least the past were pass'd away—
    And for the future—(but I write this reeling,
Having got drunk exceedingly to-day,
    So that I seem to stand upon the ceiling)
I say—the future is a serious matter—
And so—for God's sake—hock and soda-water!

HAIDÉE

When Juan woke he found some good things ready,
   A bath, a breakfast, and the finest eyes
That ever made a youthful heart less steady,
   Besides her maid's, as pretty for their size;
But I have spoken of all this already—
   And repetition's tiresome and unwise,—
Well—Juan, after bathing in the sea,
Came always back to coffee and Haidée.

Both were so young, and one so innocent,
   That bathing pass'd for nothing: Juan seem'd
To her, as 'twere, the kind of being sent,
   Of whom these two years she had nightly dream'd,
A something to be loved, a creature meant
   To be her happiness, and whom she deem'd
To render happy: all who joy would win
Must share it,—Happiness was born a twin.

It was such pleasure to behold him, such
   Enlargement of existence to partake
Nature with him, to thrill beneath his touch,
   To watch him slumbering, and to see him wake;
To live with him for ever were too much;
   But then the thought of parting made her quake:
He was her own, her ocean-treasure, cast
Like a rich wreck—her first love, and her last.

And thus a moon roll'd on, and fair Haidée
   Paid daily visits to her boy, and took

Such plentiful precautions, that still he
    Remain'd unknown within his craggy nook;
At last her father's prows put out to sea,
    For certain merchantmen upon the look,
Not as of yore to carry off an Io,
But three Ragusan vessels bound for Scio.

Then came her freedom, for she had no mother,
    So that, her father being at sea, she was
Free as a married woman, or such other
    Female, as where she likes may freely pass,
Without even the encumbrance of a brother,
    The freest she that ever gazed on glass:
I speak of Christian lands in this comparison,
Where wives, at least, are seldom kept in garrison.

Now she prolong'd her visits and her talk
    (For they must talk), and he had learnt to say
So much as to propose to take a walk,—
    For little had he wander'd since the day
On which, like a young flower snapp'd from the stalk,
    Drooping and dewy on the beach he lay,—
And thus they walk'd out in the afternoon,
And saw the sun set opposite the moon.

It was a wild and breaker-beaten coast,
    With cliffs above, and a broad sandy shore,
Guarded by shoals and rocks as by an host,
    With here and there a creek, whose aspect wore
A better welcome to the tempest-tost;

And rarely ceased the haughty billow's roar,
Save on the dead long summer days, which make
The outstretch'd ocean glitter like a lake.

And the small ripple spilt upon the beach
    Scarcely o'erpass'd the cream of your champagne,
When o'er the brim the sparkling bumpers reach,
    That spring-dew of the spirit! the heart's rain!
Few things surpass old wine; and they may preach
    Who please,—the more because they preach in vain,—
Let us have wine and women, mirth and laughter,
Sermons and soda-water the day after.

Man, being reasonable, must get drunk;
    The best of life is but intoxication:
Glory, the grape, love, gold, in these are sunk
    The hopes of all men, and of every nation;
Without their sap, how branchless were the trunk
    Of life's strange tree, so fruitful on occasion!
But to return,—Get very drunk; and when
You wake with headache, you shall see what then.

Ring for your valet—bid him quickly bring
    Some hock and soda-water, then you'll know
A pleasure worthy Xerxes the great king;
    For not the blest sherbet, sublimed with snow,
Nor the first sparkle of the desert spring,
    Nor Burgundy in all its sunset glow,
After long travel, ennui, love, or slaughter,
Vie with that draught of hock and soda-water.

The coast—I think it was the coast that I
    Was just describing—Yes, it *was* the coast—
Lay at this period quiet as the sky,
    The sands untumbled, the blue waves untost,
And all was stillness, save the sea-bird's cry,
    And dolphin's leap, and little billow crost
By some low rock or shelve, that made it fret
Against the boundary it scarcely wet.

And forth they wander'd, her sire being gone,
    As I have said, upon an expedition;
And mother, brother, guardian, she had none,
    Save Zoe, who, although with due precision
She waited on her lady with the sun,
    Thought daily service was her only mission,
Bringing warm water, wreathing her long tresses,
And asking now and then for cast-off dresses.

It was the cooling hour, just when the rounded
    Red sun sinks down behind the azure hill,
Which then seems as if the whole earth it bounded,
    Circling all nature, hush'd, and dim, and still,
With the far mountain-crescent half surrounded
    On one side, and the deep sea calm and chill,
Upon the other, and the rosy sky,
With one star sparkling through it like an eye.

And thus they wander'd forth, and hand in hand,
    Over the shining pebbles and the shells,
Glided along the smooth and harden'd sand,
    And in the worn and wild receptacles
Work'd by the storms, yet work'd as it were plann'd,

In hollow halls, with sparry roofs and cells,
They turn'd to rest; and, each clasp'd by an arm,
Yielded to the deep twilight's purple charm.

They look'd up to the sky, whose floating glow
    Spread like a rosy ocean, vast and bright;
They gazed upon the glittering sea below,
    Whence the broad moon rose circling into sight;
They heard the waves splash, and the wind so low,
    And saw each other's dark eyes darting light
Into each other—and, beholding this,
Their lips drew near, and clung into a kiss;

A long, long kiss, a kiss of youth, and love,
    And beauty, all concentrating like rays
Into one focus, kindled from above;
    Such kisses as belong to early days,
Where heart, and soul, and sense, in concert move,
    And the blood's lava, and the pulse a blaze,
Each kiss a heart-quake,—for a kiss's strength,
I think it must be reckon'd by its length.

By length I mean duration; theirs endured
    Heaven knows how long—no doubt they never reck-
        on'd;
And if they had, they could not have secured
    The sum of their sensations to a second:
They had not spoken; but they felt allured,
    As if their souls and lips each other beckon'd,
Which, being join'd, like swarming bees they clung—
Their hearts the flowers from whence the honey sprung.

They were alone, but not alone as they
   Who shut in chambers think it loneliness;
The silent ocean, and the starlight bay,
   The twilight glow, which momently grew less,
The voiceless sands, and dropping caves, that lay
   Around them, made them to each other press,
As if there were no life beneath the sky
Save theirs, and that their life could never die.

They fear'd no eyes nor ears on that lone beach,
They felt no terrors from the night; they were
All in all to each other; though their speech
   Was broken words, they *thought* a language there,—
And all the burning tongues the passions teach
   Found in one sigh the best interpreter
Of nature's oracle—first love,—that all
Which Eve has left her daughters since her fall.

Haldée spoke not of scruples, ask'd no vows,
   Nor offer'd any; she had never heard
Of plight and promises to be a spouse,
   Or perils by a loving maid incurr'd;
She was all which pure ignorance allows,
   And flew to her young mate like a young bird,
And never having dreamt of falsehood, she
Had not one word to say of constancy.

She loved, and was beloved—she adored,
   And she was worshipp'd; after nature's fashion,
Their intense souls, into each other pour'd,
   If souls could die, had perish'd in that passion,—
But by degrees their senses were restored,

Again to be o'ercome, again to dash on;
And, beating 'gainst *his* bosom. Haidée's heart
Felt as if never more to beat apart.

Alas! they were so young, so beautiful,
  So lonely, loving, helpless, and the hour
Was that in which the heart is always full,
  And, having o'er itself no further power,
Prompts deeds eternity cannot annul,
  But pays off moments in an endless shower
Of hell-fire—all prepared for people giving
Pleasure or pain to one another living.

Alas! for Juan and Haidée! they were
  So loving and so lovely—till then never,
Excepting our first parents, such a pair
  Had run the risk of being damn'd for ever;
And Haidée, being devout as well as fair,
  Had, doubtless, heard about the Stygian river,
And hell and purgatory—but forgot
Just in the very crisis she should not.

They look upon each other, and their eyes
  Gleam in the moonlight; and her white arm clasps
Round Juan's head, and his around her lies
  Half buried in the tresses which it grasps;
She sits upon his knee, and drinks his sighs,
  He hers, until they end in broken gasps;
And thus they form a group that's quite antique,
Half naked, loving, natural, and Greek.

                          From *Don Juan,* Canto II

THE ISLES OF GREECE

The isles of Greece, the isles of Greece!
  Where burning Sappho loved and sung,
Where grew the arts of war and peace,
  Where Delos rose, and Phœbus sprung!
Eternal summer gilds them yet,
But all, except their sun, is set.

The Scian and the Teian muse,
  The hero's harp, the lover's lute,
Have found the fame your shores refuse:
  Their place of birth alone is mute
To sounds which echo further west
Than your sires' 'Islands of the Blest.'

The mountains look on Marathon—
  And Marathon looks on the sea;
And musing there an hour alone,
  I dream'd that Greece might still be free;
For standing on the Persians' grave,
I could not deem myself a slave.

A king sate on the rocky brow
  Which looks o'er sea-born Salamis;
And ships, by thousands, lay below,
  And men in nations;—all were his!
He counted them at break of day—
And when the sun set where were they?

And where are they? and where art thou,
  My country? On thy voiceless shore

The heroic lay is tuneless now—
  The heroic bosom beats no more!
And must thy lyre, so long divine,
Degenerate into hands like mine?

'Tis something, in the dearth of fame,
  Though link'd among a fetter'd race,
To feel at least a patriot's shame,
  Even as I sing, suffuse my face;
For what is left the poet here?
For Greeks a blush—for Greece a tear.

Must *we* but weep o'er days more blest?
  Must *we* but blush?—Our fathers bled.
Earth! render back from out thy breast
  A remnant of our Spartan dead!
Of the three hundred grant but three,
To make a new Thermopylæ!

What, silent still? and silent all?
  Ah! no;—the voices of the dead
Sound like a distant torrent's fall,
  And answer, 'Let one living head,
But one arise,—we come, we come!'
'Tis but the living who are dumb.

In vain—in vain: strike other chords;
  Fill high the cup with Samian wine!
Leave battles to the Turkish hordes,
  And shed the blood of Scio's vine!
Hark! rising to the ignoble call—
How answers each bold Bacchanal!

You have the Pyrrhic dance as yet;
　Where is the Pyrrhic phalanx gone?
Of two such lessons, why forget
　The nobler and the manlier one?
You have the letters Cadmus gave—
Think ye he meant them for a slave?

Fill high the bowl with Samian wine!
　We will not think of themes like these!
It made Anacreon's song divine:
　He served—but served Polycrates—
A tyrant; but our masters then
Were still, at least, our countrymen.

The tyrant of the Chersonese
　Was freedom's best and bravest friend;
That tyrant was Miltiades!
　Oh! that the present hour would lend
Another despot of the kind!
Such chains as his were sure to bind.

Fill high the bowl with Samian wine!
　On Suli's rock, and Parga's shore,
Exists the remnant of a line
　Such as the Doric mothers bore;
And there, perhaps, some seed is sown,
The Heracleidan blood might own.

Trust not for freedom to the Franks—
　They have a king who buys and sells;
In native swords, and native ranks,

The only hope of courage dwells:
But Turkish force, and Latin fraud,
Would break your shield, however broad.

Fill high the bowl with Samian wine!
　　Our virgins dance beneath the shade—
I see their glorious black eyes shine;
　　But gazing on each glowing maid,
My own the burning tear-drop laves,
To think such breasts must suckle slaves.

Place me on Sunium's marbled steep,
　　Where nothing, save the waves and I,
May hear our mutual murmurs sweep;
　　There, swan-like, let me sing and die:
A land of slaves shall ne'er be mine—
Dash down yon cup of Samian wine!

From *Don Juan,* Canto III

OF ALL THE BARBAROUS MIDDLE AGES

Of all the barbarous middle ages, that
   Which is most barbarous is the middle age
Of man! it is—I really scarce know what;
   But when we hover between fool and sage,
And don't know justly what we would be at—
   A period something like a printed page,
Black letter upon foolscap, while our hair
Grows grizzled, and we are not what we were;—

Too old for youth,—too young, at thirty-five,
   To herd with boys, or hoard with good three-
     score,—
I wonder people should be left alive;
   But since they are, that epoch is a bore:
Love lingers still, although 'twere late to wive:
   And as for other love, the illusion's o'er;
And money, that most pure imagination,
Gleams only through the dawn of its creation.

O Gold! Why call we misers miserable?
   Theirs is the pleasure that can never pall;
Theirs is the best bower anchor, the chain cable
   Which holds fast other pleasures great and small.
Ye who but see the saving man at table,
   And scorn his temperate board, as none at all,
And wonder how the wealthy can be sparing,
Know not what visions spring from each cheese-
     paring.

Love or lust makes man sick, and wine much
    sicker;
    Ambition rends, and gaming gains a loss;
But making money, slowly first, then quicker,
    And adding still a little through each cross
(Which *will* come over things), beats love or liquor,
    The gamester's counter, or the statesman's *dross*.
O Gold! I still prefer thee unto paper,
Which makes bank credit like a bank of *vapour*.

From *Don Juan*, Canto XII

BEPPO

BEPPO

A VENETIAN STORY

'Tis known, at least it should be, that throughout
    All countries of the Catholic persuasion,
Some weeks before Shrove Tuesday comes about,
    The people take their fill of recreation,
And buy repentance, ere they grow devout,
    However high their rank, or low their station,
With fiddling, feasting, dancing, drinking, masking,
And other things which may be had for asking.

The moment night with dusky mantle covers
    The skies (and the more duskily the better),
The time less liked by husbands than by lovers
    Begins, and prudery flings aside her fetter;
And gaiety on restless tiptoe hovers,
    Giggling with all the gallants who beset her;
And there are songs and quavers, roaring, humming,
Guitars, and every other sort of strumming.

And there are dresses splendid, but fantastical,
    Masks of all times and nations, Turks and Jews,
And harlequins and clowns, with feats gymnastical,
    Greeks, Romans, Yankee-doodles, and Hindoos;
All kinds of dress, except the ecclesiastical,

All people, as their fancies hit, may choose,
But no one in these parts may quiz the clergy,—
Therefore take heed, ye Freethinkers! I charge ye.

You'd better walk about begirt with briars,
    Instead of coat and smallclothes, than put on
A single stitch reflecting upon friars,
    Although you swore it only was in fun;
They'd haul you o'er the coals, and stir the fires
    Of Phlegethon with every mother's son,
Nor say one mass to cool the caldron's bubble
That boil'd your bones, unless you paid them double.

But saving this, you may put on whate'er
    You like by way of doublet, cape, or cloak,
Such as in Monmouth-street, or in Rag Fair,
    Would rig you out in seriousness or joke;
And even in Italy such places are,
    With prettier name in softer accents spoke,
For, bating Covent Garden, I can hit on
No place that's called 'Piazza' in Great Britain.

This feast is named the Carnival, which being
    Interpreted, implies 'farewell to flesh':
So call'd, because the name and thing agreeing,
    Through Lent they live on fish both salt and fresh.
But why they usher Lent with so much glee in,
    Is more than I can tell, although I guess
'Tis as we take a glass with friends at parting.
In the stage-coach or packet, just at starting.

And thus they bid farewell to carnal dishes,
   And solid meats, and highly spiced ragouts,
To live for forty days on ill-dress'd fishes,
   Because they have no sauces to their stews;
A thing which causes many 'poohs' and 'pishes,'
   And several oaths (which would not suit the Muse),
From travellers accustom'd from a boy
To eat their salmon, at the least, with soy;

And therefore humbly I would recommend
   'The curious in fish-sauce,' before they cross

The sea, to bid their cook, or wife, or friend,
　　Walk or ride to the Strand, and buy in gross
(Or if set out beforehand, these may send
　　By any means least liable to loss)
Ketchup, Soy, Chili-vinegar, and Harvey,
Or by the Lord! a Lent will well nigh starve ye;

That is to say, if your religion's Roman,
　　And you at Rome would do as Romans do,
According to the proverb,—although no man,
　　If foreign, is obliged to fast; and you
If Protestant, or sickly, or a woman,
　　Would rather dine in sin on a ragout—
Dine and be d—d! I don't mean to be coarse,
But that's the penalty, to say no worse.

Of all the places where the Carnival
　　Was most facetious in the days of yore,
For dance, and song, and serenade, and ball,
　　And masque, and mime, and mystery, and more
Than I have time to tell now, or at all,
　　Venice the bell from every city bore,—
And at the moment when I fix my story,
That sea-born city was in all her glory.

They've pretty faces yet, those same Venetians,
　　Black eyes, arch'd brows, and sweet expressions still;
Such as of old were copied from the Grecians,
　　In ancient arts by moderns mimick'd ill;
And like so many Venuses of Titian's
　　(The best's at Florence—see it, if ye will),

They look when leaning over the balcony,
Or stepp'd from out a picture by Giorgione,

Whose tints are truth and beauty at their best;
    And when you to Manfrini's palace go,
That picture (howsoever fine the rest)
    Is loveliest to my mind of all the show;
It may perhaps be also to *your* zest,
    And that's the cause I rhyme upon it so:
'Tis but a portrait of his son, and wife,
And self; but *such* a woman! love in life!

Love in full life and length, not love ideal,
    No, nor ideal beauty, that fine name,
But something better still, so very real,
    That the sweet model must have been the same;
A thing that you would purchase, beg, or steal,
    Were't not impossible, besides a shame:
The face recalls some face, as 'twere with pain,
You once have seen, but ne'er will see again.

One of those forms which flit by us, when we
    Are young, and fix our eyes on every face;
And, oh! the loveliness at times we see
    In momentary gliding, the soft grace,
The youth, the bloom, the beauty which agree,
    In many a nameless being we retrace,
Whose course and home we knew not, nor shall know,
Like the lost Pleiad seen no more below.

I said that like a picture by Giorgione
　　Venetian women were, and so they *are,*
Particularly seen from a balcony
　　(For beauty's sometimes best set off afar),
And there, just like a heroine of Goldoni,
　　They peep from out the blind, or o'er the bar;
And truth to say, they're mostly very pretty,
And rather like to show it, more's the pity!

For glances beget ogles, ogles sighs,
　　Sighs wishes, wishes words, and words a letter,
Which flies on wings of light-heel'd Mercuries,
　　Who do such things because they know no better;
And then, God knows what mischief may arise,
　　When love links two young people in one fetter,
Vile assignations, and adulterous beds,
Elopements, broken vows, and hearts, and heads.

Shakespeare described the sex in Desdemona
　　As very fair, but yet suspect in fame,
And to this day from Venice to Verona
　　Such matters may be probably the same,
Except that since those times was never known a
　　Husband whom mere suspicion could inflame
To suffocate a wife no more than twenty,
Because she had a 'cavalier servente.'

Their jealousy (if they are ever jealous)
　　Is of a fair complexion altogether,
Not like that sooty devil of Othello's,
　　Which smothers women in a bed of feather,

But worthier of these much more jolly fellows,
   When weary of the matrimonial tether
His head for such a wife no mortal bothers,
But takes at once another, or another's.

Didst ever see a Gondola? For fear
   You should not, I'll describe it you exactly:
'Tis a long cover'd boat that's common here
   Carved at the prow, built lightly, but compactly,
Row'd by two rowers, each call'd 'Gondolier,'
   It glides along the water looking blackly,
Just like a coffin clapt in a canoe,
Where none can make out what you say or do.

And up and down the long canals they go,
   And under the Rialto shoot along,
By night and day, all paces, swift or slow,
   And round the theatres, a sable throng,
They wait in their dusk livery of woe,—
   But not to them do woeful things belong,
For sometimes they contain a deal of fun,
Like mourning coaches when the funeral's done.

But to my story.—'Twas some years ago,
   It may be thirty, forty, more or less,
The Carnival was at its height, and so
   Were all kinds of buffoonery and dress;
A certain lady went to see the show,
   Her real name I know not, nor can guess,
And so we'll call her Laura, if you please,
Because it slips into my verse with ease.

She was not old, nor young, nor at the years
    Which certain people call a *'certain age,'*
Which yet the most uncertain age appears,
    Because I never heard, nor could engage
A person yet by prayers, or bribes, or tears,
    To name, define by speech, or write on page,
The period meant precisely by that word,—
Which surely is exceedingly absurd.

Laura was blooming still, had made the best
    Of time, and time return'd the compliment,

And treated her genteelly, so that, dress'd,
　　She look'd extremely well where'er she went;
A pretty woman is a welcome guest,
　　And Laura's brow a frown had rarely bent;
Indeed, she shone all smiles, and seem'd to flatter
Mankind with her black eyes for looking at her.

She was a married woman; 'tis convenient,
　　Because in Christian countries 'tis a rule
To view their little slips with eyes more lenient;
　　Whereas if single ladies play the fool
(Unless within the period intervenient
　　A well-timed wedding makes the scandal cool),
I don't know how they ever can get over it,
Except they manage never to discover it.

Her husband sail'd upon the Adriatic,
　　And made some voyages, too, in other seas,
And when he lay in quarantine for pratique
　　(A forty days' precaution 'gainst disease),
His wife would mount, at times, her highest attic,
　　For thence she could discern the ship with ease:
He was a merchant trading to Aleppo,
His name Giuseppe, call'd more briefly, Beppo.

He was a man as dusky as a Spaniard,
　　Sunburnt with travel, yet a portly figure;
Though colour'd, as it were, within a tanyard,
　　He was a person both of sense and vigour—
A better seaman never yet did man yard;
　　And she, although her manners show'd no rigour,

Was deem'd a woman of the strictest principle,
So much as to be thought almost invincible.

But several years elapsed since they had met;
    Some people thought the ship was lost, and some
That he had somehow blunder'd into debt,
    And did not like the thought of steering home;
And there were several offer'd any bet,
    Or that he would, or that he would not come;
For most men (till by losing render'd sager)
Will back their own opinions with a wager.

'Tis said that their last parting was pathetic,
    As partings often are, or ought to be,
And their presentiment was quite prophetic,
    That they should never more each other see,
(A sort of morbid feeling, half poetic,
    Which I have known occur in two or three,)
When kneeling on the shore upon her sad knee
He left this Adriatic Ariadne.

And Laura waited long, and wept a little,
    And thought of wearing weeds, as well she might;
She almost lost all appetite for victual,
    And could not sleep with ease alone at night;
She deem'd the window-frames and shutters brittle
    Against a daring housebreaker or sprite,
And so she thought it prudent to connect her
With a vice-husband, *chiefly* to *protect her*.

She chose, (and what is there they will not choose,
    If only you will but oppose their choice?)
Till Beppo should return from his long cruise,
    And bid once more her faithful heart rejoice,
A man some women like, and yet abuse—
    A coxcomb was he by the public voice;
A Count of wealth, they said, as well as quality,
And in his pleasures of great liberality.

And then he was a Count, and then he knew
    Music, and dancing, fiddling, French and Tuscan;
The last not easy, be it known to you,
    For few Italians speak the right Etruscan.
He was a critic upon operas, too,
    And knew all niceties of the sock and buskin;
And no Venetian audience could endure a
Song, scene, or air, when he cried 'seccatura!'

His 'bravo' was decisive, for that sound
    Hush'd 'Academie' sigh'd in silent awe;
The fiddlers trembled as he look'd around,
    For fear of some false note's detected flaw;
The 'prima donna's' tuneful heart would bound,
    Dreading the deep damnation of his 'bah!'
Soprano, basso, even the contra-alto,
Wish'd him five fathom under the Rialto.

He patronised the Improvisatori,
    Nay, could himself extemporise some stanzas,
Wrote rhymes, sang songs, could also tell a story,
    Sold pictures, and was skilful in the dance as

Italians can be, though in this their glory
    Must surely yield the palm to that which France has;
In short, he was a perfect cavaliero,
And to his very valet seem'd a hero.

Then he was faithful too, as well as amorous;
    So that no sort of female could complain,
Although they're now and then a little clamorous,
    He never put the pretty souls in pain;
His heart was one of those which most enamour us,
    Wax to receive, and marble to retain:
He was a lover of the good old school,
Who still become more constant as they cool.

No wonder such accomplishments should turn
    A female head, however sage and steady—
With scarce a hope that Beppo could return,
    In law he was almost as good as dead, he
Nor sent, nor wrote, nor show'd the least concern,
    And she had waited several years already;
And really if a man won't let us know
That he's alive, he's *dead,* or should be so.

Besides, within the Alps, to every woman,
    (Although, God knows, it is a grievous sin,)
'Tis, I may say, permitted to have *two* men;
    I can't tell who first brought the custom in,
But 'Cavalier Serventes' are quite common,
    And no one notices nor cares a pin;
And we may call this (not to say the worst)
A *second* marriage which corrupts the *first.*

The word was formerly a 'Cicisbeo,'
    But *that* is now grown vulgar and indecent;
The Spaniards call the person a *'Cortejo,'*
    For the same mode subsists in Spain, though recent;
In short, it reaches from the Po to Teio,
    And may perhaps at last be o'er the sea sent:
But Heaven preserve Old England from such courses!
Or what becomes of damage and divorces?

However, I still think, with all due deference
    To the fair *single* part of the creation,
That married ladies should preserve the preference
    In *tête-à-tête* or general conversation—
And this I say without peculiar reference
    To England, France, or any other nation—
Because they know the world, and are at ease,
And being natural, naturally please.

'Tis true, your budding Miss is very charming,
    But shy and awkward at first coming out,
So much alarm'd, that she is quite alarming,
    All Giggle, Blush; half Pertness, and half Pout;
And glancing at *Mamma,* for fear there's harm in
    What you, she, it, or they, may be about,
The nursery still lisps out in all they utter—
Besides, they always smell of bread and butter.

But 'Cavalier Servente' is the phrase
    Used in politest circles to express
This supernumerary slave, who stays
    Close to the lady as a part of dress,

Her word the only law which he obeys.
    His is no sinecure, as you may guess;
Coach, servants, gondola, he goes to call,
And carries fan and tippet, gloves and shawl.

With all its sinful doings, I must say,
    That Italy's a pleasant place to me,
Who love to see the Sun shine every day,
    And vines (not nail'd to walls) from tree to tree
Festoon'd, much like the back scene of a play,
    Or melodrame, which people flock to see,
When the first act is ended by a dance
In vineyards copied from the south of France.

I like on Autumn evenings to ride out,
    Without being forced to bid my groom be sure
My cloak is round his middle strapp'd about,
    Because the skies are not the most secure;
I know too that, if stopp'd upon my route,
    Where the green alleys windingly allure,
Reeling with grapes red waggons choke the way,—
In England 'twould be dung, dust, or a dray.

I also like to dine on becaficas,
    To see the Sun set, sure he'll rise tomorrow,
Not through a misty morning twinkling weak as
    A drunken man's dead eye in maudlin sorrow,
But with all Heaven t'himself; the day will break as
    Beauteous as cloudless, nor be forced to borrow
That sort of farthing candlelight which glimmers
Where reeking London's smoky caldron simmers.

I love the language, that soft bastard Latin,
    Which melts like kisses from a female mouth,
And sounds as if it should be writ on satin,
    With syllables which breathe of the sweet South,
And gentle liquids gliding all so pat in,
    That not a single accent seems uncouth,
Like our harsh northern whistling, grunting guttural,
Which we're obliged to hiss, and spit, and sputter all.

I like the women too (forgive my folly),
    From the rich peasant cheek of ruddy bronze,
And large black eyes that flash on you a volley
    Of rays that say a thousand things at once,
To the high dama's brow, more melancholy,
    But clear, and with a wild and liquid glance,
Heart on her lips, and soul within her eyes,
Soft as her clime, and sunny as her skies.

Eve of the land which still is Paradise!
    Italian beauty! didst thou not inspire
Raphael, who died in thy embrace, and vies
    With all we know of Heaven, or can desire,
In what he hath bequeath'd us?—in what guise,
    Though flashing from the fervour of the lyre,
Would *words* describe thy past and present glow,
While yet Canova can create below?

'England! with all thy faults I love thee still,'
    I said at Calais, and have not forgot it;
I like to speak and lucubrate my fill;
    I like the government (but that is not it);

I like the freedom of the press and quill;
   I like the Habeas Corpus (when we've got it);
I like a parliamentary debate,
Particularly when 'tis not too late;

I like the taxes, when they're not too many;
   I like a seacoal fire, when not too dear;
I like a beef-steak, too, as well as any;
   Have no objection to a pot of beer;
I like the weather, when it is not rainy,
   That is, I like two months of every year,
And so God save the Regent, Church, and King!
Which means that I like all and everything.

Our standing army, and disbanded seamen,
   Poor's rate, Reform, my own, the nation's debt,
Our little riots just to show we are free men,
   Our trifling bankruptcies in the Gazette,
Our cloudy climate, and our chilly women,
   All these I can forgive, and those forget,
And greatly venerate our recent glories,
And wish they were not owing to the Tories.

But to my tale of Laura,—for I find
   Digression is a sin, that by degrees
Becomes exceeding tedious to my mind,
   And, therefore, may the reader too displease—
The gentle reader, who may wax unkind,
   And caring little for the author's ease,
Insist on knowing what he means, a hard
And hapless situation for a bard.

Oh that I had the art of easy writing
  What should be easy reading! could I scale
Parnassus, where the Muses sit inditing
  Those pretty poems never known to fail,
How quickly would I print (the world delighting)
  A Grecian, Syrian, or Assyrian tale;
And sell you, mix'd with western sentimentalism,
Some samples of the finest Orientalism!

But I am but a nameless sort of person,
  (A broken Dandy lately on my travels)
And take for rhyme, to hook my rambling verse on,
  The first that Walker's Lexicon unravels,
And when I can't find that, I put a worse on,
  Not caring as I ought for critics' cavils;
I've half a mind to tumble down to prose,
But verse is more in fashion—so here goes.

The Count and Laura made their new arrangement,
  Which lasted, as arrangements sometimes do,
For half a dozen years without estrangement;
  They had their little differences, too;
Those jealous whiffs, which never any change meant;
  In such affairs there probably are few
Who have not had this pouting sort of squabble,
From sinners of high station to the rabble.

But, on the whole, they were a happy pair,
  As happy as unlawful love could make them;
The gentleman was fond, the lady fair,
  Their chains so slight, 'twas not worth while to
    break them;

The world beheld them with indulgent air;
　　The pious only wish'd 'the devil take them!'
He took them not; he very often waits,
And leaves old sinners to be young ones' baits.

But they were young: Oh! what without our youth
　　Would love be! What would youth be without love!
Youth lends it joy, and sweetness, vigour, truth,
　　Heart, soul, and all that seems as from above;
But, languishing with years, it grows uncouth—
　　One of few things experience don't improve,
Which is, perhaps, the reason why old fellows
Are always so preposterously jealous.

It was the Carnival, as I have said
　　Some six and thirty stanzas back, and so
Laura the usual preparations made,
　　Which you do when your mind's made up to go
To-night to Mrs. Boehm's masquerade,
　　Spectator, or partaker in the show;
The only difference known between the cases
Is—*here,* we have six weeks of 'varnish'd faces.'

Laura, when dress'd, was (as I sang before)
　　A pretty woman as was ever seen,
Fresh as the Angel o'er a new inn door,
　　Or frontispiece of a new Magazine,
With all the fashions which the last month wore,
　　Colour'd, and silver paper leaved between
That and the title-page, for fear the press
Should soil with parts of speech the parts of dress.

They went to the Ridotto;—'tis a hall
　　Where people dance, and sup, and dance again;
Its proper name, perhaps, were a masqued ball,
　　But that's of no importance to my strain;
'Tis (on a smaller scale) like our Vauxhall,
　　Excepting that it can't be spoilt by rain;
The company is 'mix'd' (the phrase I quote is
As much as saying they're below your notice);

For a 'mix'd company' implies that, save
　　Yourself and friends, and half a hundred more,
Whom you may bow to without looking grave,
　　The rest are but a vulgar set, the bore
Of public places, where they basely brave
　　The fashionable stare of twenty score
　　Of well-bred persons, call'd *'The World;'* but I,
Although I know them, really don't know why.

This is the case in England; at least was
　　During the dynasty of Dandies, now
Perchance succeeded by some other class
　　Of imitated imitators:—how
Irreparably soon decline, alas!
　　The demagogues of fashion: all below
Is frail; how easily the world is lost
By love, or war, and now and then by frost!

Crush'd was Napoleon by the northern Thor,
　　Who knock'd his army down with icy hammer,
Stopp'd by the *elements*, like a whaler, or
　　A blundering novice in his new French grammar;

Good cause had he to doubt the chance of war,
   And as for Fortune—but I dare not d—n her,
Because, were I to ponder to infinity,
The more I should believe in her divinity.

She rules the present, past, and all to be yet,
   She gives us luck in lotteries, love, and marriage;
I cannot say that she's done much for me yet;
   Not that I mean her bounties to disparage,
We've not yet closed accounts, and we shall see yet
   How much she'll make amends for past miscarriage.
Meantime the Goddess I'll no more importune,
Unless to thank her when she's made my fortune.

To turn,—and to return;—the devil take it!
   This story slips for ever through my fingers,
Because, just as the stanza likes to make it,
   It needs must be, and so it rather lingers:
This form of verse began, I can't well break it,
   But must keep time and tune like public singers;
But if I once get through my present measure,
I'll take another when I'm next at leisure.

They went to the Ridotto ('tis a place
   To which I mean to go myself to-morrow,
Just to divert my thoughts a little space,
   Because I'm rather hippish, and may borrow
Some spirits, guessing at what kind of face,
   May lurk beneath each mask; and as my sorrow
Slackens its pace sometimes, I'll make, or find,
Something shall leave it half an hour behind.)

Now Laura moves along the joyous crowd,
    Smiles in her eyes, and simpers on her lips;
To some she whispers, others speaks aloud;
    To some she curtsies, and to some she dips,
Complains of warmth, and this complaint avow'd,
    Her lover brings the lemonade, she sips;
She then surveys, condemns, but pities still
Her dearest friends for being dress'd so ill.

One has false curls, another too much paint,
    A third—where did she buy that frightful turban?
A fourth's so pale she fears she's going to faint,
    A fifth's look's vulgar, dowdyish, and suburban,
A sixth's white silk has got a yellow taint,
    A seventh's thin muslin surely will be her bane,
And lo! an eighth appears,—'I'll see no more!'
For fear, like Banquo's kings, they reach a score.

Meantime, while she was thus at others gazing,
    Others were levelling their looks at her;
She heard the men's half-whisper'd mode of praising,
    And, till 'twas done, determined not to stir;
The women only thought it quite amazing
    That, at her time of life, so many were
Admirers still,—but men are so debased,
Those brazen creatures always suit their taste.

For my part, now, I ne'er could understand
    Why naughty women—but I won't discuss
A thing which is a scandal to the land,
    I only don't see why it should be thus;

And if I were but in a gown and band,
    Just to entitle me to make a fuss,
I'd preach on this till Wilberforce and Romilly
Should quote in their next speeches from my homily.

While Laura thus was seen, and seeing, smiling,
    Talking, she knew not why, and cared not what,
So that her female friends, with envy broiling,
    Beheld her airs and triumph, and all that;
And well-dress'd males still kept before her filing,
    And passing bow'd and mingled with her chat;
More than the rest one person seem'd to stare
With pertinacity that's rather rare.

He was a Turk, the colour of mahogany;
    And Laura saw him, and at first was glad,
Because the Turks so much admire philogyny,
    Although their usage of their wives is sad;
'Tis said they use no better than a dog any
    Poor woman, whom they purchase like a pad;
They have a number, though they ne'er exhibit 'em,
Four wives by law, and concubines 'ad libitum.'

They lock them up, and veil, and guard them daily,
    They scarcely can behold their male relations,
So that their moments do not pass so gaily
    As is supposed the case with northern nations;
Confinement, too, must make them look quite palely;
    And as the Turks abhor long conversations,
Their days are either pass'd in doing nothing,
Or bathing, nursing, making love, and clothing.

They cannot read, and so don't lisp in criticism;
    Nor write, and so they don't affect the muse;
Were never caught in epigram or witticism,
    Have no romances, sermons, plays, reviews,—
In harams learning soon would make a pretty schism,
    But luckily these beauties are no 'Blues;'
No bustling Botherbys have they to show 'em
'That charming passage in the last new poem:'

No solemn, antique gentleman of rhyme,
    Who having angled all his life for fame,
And getting but a nibble at a time,
    Still fussily keeps fishing on, the same
Small 'Triton of the minnows,' the sublime
    Of mediocrity, the furious tame,
The echo's echo, usher of the school
Of female wits, boy bards—in short, a fool!

A stalking oracle of awful phrase.
    The approving 'Good!' (by no means GOOD in law,)
Humming like flies around the newest blaze,
    The bluest of bluebottles you e'er saw,
Teasing with blame, excruciating with praise,
    Gorging the little fame he gets all raw,
Translating tongues he knows not even by letter,
And sweating plays so middling, bad were better.

One hates an author that's *all author,* fellows
    In foolscap uniforms turn'd up with ink,
So very anxious, clever, fine, and jealous.
    One don't know what to say to them, or think,

Unless to puff them with a pair of bellows;
    Of coxcombry's worst coxcombs e'en the pink
Are preferable to these shreds of paper,
These unquench'd snuffings of the midnight taper.

Of these same we see several, and of others,
    Men of the world, who know the world like men,
Scott, Rogers, Moore, and all the better brothers,
    Who think of something else besides the pen;
But for the children of the 'mighty mother's,'
    The would-be wits, and can't-be gentlemen,
I leave them to their daily 'tea is ready,'
Smug coterie, and literary lady.

The poor dear Mussulwomen whom I mention
    Have none of these instructive pleasant people,
And *one* would seem to them a new invention,
    Unknown as bells within a Turkish steeple;
I think 'twould almost be worth while to pension
    (Though best-sown projects very often reap ill)
A missionary author, just to preach
Our Christian usage of the parts of speech.

No chemistry for them unfolds her gases,
    No metaphysics are let loose in lectures,
No circulating library amasses
    Religious novels, moral tales, and strictures
Upon the living manners, as they pass us;
    No exhibition glares with annual pictures;
They stare not on the stars from out their attics,
Nor deal (thank God for that!) in mathematics.

Why I thank God for that is no great matter,
  I have my reasons, you no doubt suppose,
And as, perhaps, they would not highly flatter,
  I'll keep them for my life (to come) in prose;
I fear I have a little turn for satire,
  And yet methinks the older that one grows
Inclines us more to laugh than scold, though laughter
Leaves us so doubly serious shortly after.

Oh, mirth and innocence! Oh, milk and water!
  Ye happy mixtures of more happy days!
In these sad centuries of sin and slaughter,
  Abominable Man no more allays
His thirst with such pure beverage. No matter,
  I love you both, and both shall have my praise:
Oh, for old Saturn's reign of sugar candy!—
Meantime I drink to your return in brandy.

Our Laura's Turk still kept his eyes upon her,
  Less in the Mussulman than Christian way,
Which seems to say, 'Madam, I do you honour,
  And while I please to stare, you'll please to stay.'
Could staring win a woman, this had won her,
  But Laura could not thus be led astray;
She had stood fire too long and well, to boggle
Even at this stranger's most outlandish ogle.

The morning now was on the point of breaking,
  A turn of time at which I would advise
Ladies who have been dancing, or partaking

In any other kind of exercise,
To make their preparations for forsaking
   The ball-room ere the sun begins to rise,
Because when once the lamps and candles fail,
His blushes make them look a little pale.

I've seen some balls and revels in my time,
   And stay'd them over for some silly reason,
And then I look'd (I hope it was no crime)
   To see what lady best stood out the season,
And though I've seen some thousands in their prime,
   Lovely and pleasing, and who still may please on,
I never saw but one (the stars withdrawn)
Whose bloom could after dancing dare the dawn.

The name of this Aurora I'll not mention,
   Although I might, for she was nought to me
More than that patent work of God's invention,
   A charming woman, whom we like to see;
But writing names would merit reprehension,
   Yet if you like to find out this fair *she,*
At the next London or Parisian ball
You still may mark her cheek out-blooming all.

Laura, who knew it would not do at all
   To meet the daylight after seven hours' sitting
Among three thousand people at a ball,
   To make her curtsy thought it right and fitting;
The Count was at her elbow with her shawl,
   And they the room were on the point of quitting,
When lo! those cursed gondoliers had got
Just in the very place where they *should not.*

In this they're like our coachmen, and the cause
    Is much the same—the crowd, and pulling, hauling,
With blasphemies enough to break their jaws,
    They make a never intermitted brawling.
At home, our Bow-street gemmen keep the laws,
    And here a sentry stands within your calling;
But for all that, there is a deal of swearing,
And nauseous words past mentioning or bearing.

The Count and Laura found their boat at last,
    And homeward floated o'er the silent tide,
Discussing all the dances gone and past;
    The dancers and their dresses, too, beside;
Some little scandals eke; but all aghast
    (As to their palace-stairs the rowers glide)
Sate Laura by the side of her Adorer,
When lo! the Mussulman was there before her.

'Sir,' said the Count, with brow exceeding grave,
    'Your unexpected presence here will make
It necessary for myself to crave
    Its import? But perhaps 'tis a mistake;
I hope it is so; and, at once to waive
    All compliment, I hope so for *your* sake;
You understand my meaning, or you *shall*.'
'Sir' (quoth the Turk), ' 'tis no mistake at all:

'That lady is *my wife!*' Much wonder paints
    The lady's changing cheek, as well it might;
But where an Englishwoman sometimes faints,
    Italian females don't do so outright;
They only call a little on their saints,

And then come to themselves, almost or quite;
Which saves much hartshorn, salts, and sprinkling faces,
And cutting stays, as usual in such cases.

She said,—what could she say? Why, not a word:
  But the Count courteously invited in
The stranger, much appeased by what he heard:
  'Such things, perhaps, we'd best discuss within,'
Said he; 'don't let us make ourselves absurd
  In public, by a scene, nor raise a din,
For then the chief and only satisfaction
Will be much quizzing on the whole transaction.'

They enter'd, and for coffee call'd—it came,
  A beverage for Turks and Christians both,
Although the way they make it's not the same.
  Now Laura, much recover'd, or less loth
To speak, cries 'Beppo! what's your pagan name?
  Bless me! your beard is of amazing growth!
And how came you to keep away so long?
Are you not sensible 'twas very wrong?

'And are you *really, truly,* now a Turk?
  With any other women did you wive?
Is't true they use their fingers for a fork?
  Well, that's the prettiest shawl—as I'm alive!
You'll give it me? They say you eat no pork.
  And how so many years did you contrive
To—Bless me! did I ever? No, I never
Saw a man grown so yellow! How's your liver?

'Beppo! that beard of yours becomes you not;
    It shall be shaved before you're a day older:
Why do you wear it? Oh! I had forgot—
    Pray don't you think the weather here is colder?
How do I look? You shan't stir from this spot
    In that queer dress, for fear that some beholder
Should find you out, and make the story known.
How short your hair is! Lord! how grey it's grown!'

What answer Beppo made to these demands
    Is more than I know. He was cast away
About where Troy stood once, and nothing stands;
    Became a slave of course, and for his pay
Had bread and bastinadoes, till some bands
    Of pirates landing in a neighbouring bay,
He join'd the rogues and prosper'd, and became
A renegado of indifferent fame.

But he grew rich, and with his riches grew so
    Keen the desire to see his home again,
He thought himself in duty bound to do so,
    And not be always thieving on the main;
Lonely he felt, at times, as Robin Crusoe,
    And so he hired a vessel come from Spain,
Bound for Corfu: she was a fine polacca,
Mann'd with twelve hands, and laden with tobacco.

Himself, and much (Heaven knows how gotten!) cash,
    He then embark'd, with risk of life and limb,
And got clear off, although the attempt was rash;

He said that *Providence* protected him—
For my part, I say nothing—lest we clash
   In our opinions:—well, the ship was trim,
Set sail, and kept her reckoning fairly on,
Except three days of calm when off Cape Bonn.

They reach'd the island, he transferr'd his lading
   And self and live stock to another bottom,
And pass'd for a true Turkey-merchant, trading
   With goods of various names, but I've forgot 'em.
However, he got off by this evading,
   Or else the people would perhaps have shot him;
And thus at Venice landed to reclaim
His wife, religion, house, and Christian name.

His wife received, the patriarch re-baptized him
   (He made the church a present, by the way);
He then threw off the garments which disguised him,
   And borrow'd the Count's smallclothes for a day:
His friends the more for his long absence prized him,
   Finding he'd wherewithal to make them gay,
With dinners, where he oft became the laugh of them,
For stories—but *I* don't believe the half of them.

Whate'er his youth had suffer'd, his old age
   With wealth and talking made him some amends;
Though Laura sometimes put him in a rage,
   I've heard the Count and he were always friends.
My pen is at the bottom of a page,
   Which being finish'd, here the story ends;
'Tis to be wish'd it had been sooner done,
But stories somehow lengthen when begun.

LETTERS

As his letters show, Byron was one of the greatest of
English letter writers, and among English poets, he has
only two, yet very different, equals: John Keats and
D. H. Lawrence, and he was as much himself and as
unique as they. Not unlike the rapidly moving, eight-
line, recklessly-rhymed stanzas of *Don Juan,* the letters
reveal a vibrant personality. The reader sees at once
why Byron attracted both men and women, why he created an archetypical image of the English "milord" on
the European continent—and this in prose that is as
fresh today as it was in the odd moments when he sat
down to write. This is the Byron who, wherever he
moved, created legends. My selection includes a Near
Eastern travelogue to his mother, a comment on Shelley's behavior in an open boat which in a curious way
seems to foreshadow his death by drowning, an affectionate letter to Thomas Moore, as well as portraits of
two Italian mistresses, and the one that describes the
Countess Guiccioli which gives us a glimpse of the last
and not least important of his love affairs.

TO HIS MOTHER
Prevesa, November 12, 1809

My Dear Mother,

I have now been some time in Turkey: this place is on the coast but I have traversed the interior of the province of Albania on a visit to the Pacha. I left Malta in the *Spider,* a brig of war, on the 21st of September, and arrived in eight days at Prevesa. I thence have been about 150 miles, as far as Tepaleen, his Highness's country palace, where I staid three days. The name of the Pacha is *Ali,* and he is considered a man of the first abilities: he governs the whole of Albania (the ancient Illyricum), Epirus, and part of Macedonia. His son, Vely Pacha, to whom he has given me letters, governs the Morea, and he has great influence in Egypt; in short, he is one of the most powerful men in the Ottoman empire. When I reached Yanina, the capital, after a journey of three days over the mountains, through a country of the most picturesque beauty, I found that Ali Pacha was with his army in Illyricum, besieging Ibrahim Pacha in the castle of Berat. He had heard that an Englishman of rank was not in his dominions, and had left orders in Yanina with the commandant to provide a house, and supply me with every kind of necessary *gratis;* and, though I have been allowed to make presents to the slaves, etc., I have not been permitted to pay for a single article of household consumption.

I rode out on the vizier's horses, and saw the palaces of himself and grandsons: they are splendid, but too much ornamented with silk and gold. I then went over the mountains through Zitza, a village with a Greek monastery (where I slept on my return), in the most beautiful situation (always excepting Cintra, in Portugal) I ever beheld. In nine days I reached Tepaleen. Our journey was much prolonged by the torrents that had fallen from the mountains, and intersected the roads. I shall never forget the singular scene on entering Tepaleen at five in the afternoon, as the sun was going down. It brought to my mind (with some change of *dress,* however) Scott's description of Branksome Castle in his *Lay,*[1] and the feudal system. The Albanians, in their dresses, (the most magnificent in the world, consisting of a long *white kilt,* gold-worked cloak, crimson velvet gold-laced jacket and waistcoat, silver-mounted pistols and daggers,) the Tarters with their high caps, the Turks in their vest pelisses and turbans, the soldiers and black slaves with the horses, the former in groups in an immense large open gallery in front of the palace, the latter placed in a kind of cloister below it, two hundred steeds ready caparisoned to move in a moment, couriers entering or passing out with despatches, the kettle-drums beating, boys calling the hour from the minaret of the mosque, altogether, with the singular appearance of the building itself, formed a new and delightful spectacle to a stranger. I was conducted to a very handsome apartment and my health inquired after by the vizier's secretary, *à-la-mode Turque.*

The next day I was introduced to Ali Pacha. I was

[1] *The Lay of the Last Minstrel,* Canto I.

dressed in a full suit of staff uniform, with a very magnificent sabre, etc. The vizier received me in a large room paved with marble; a fountain was playing in the centre; the apartment was surrounded by scarlet ottomans. He received me standing, a wonderful compliment from a Mussulman, and made me sit down on his right hand. I have a Greek interpreter for general use, but a physician of Ali's named Femlario, who understands Latin, acted for me on this occasion. His first question was, why, at so early an age, I left my country? —(the Turks have no idea of travelling for amusement). He then said, the English minister, Captain Leake,[2] had told him I was of a great family, and desired his respects to my mother; which I now, in the name of Ali Pacha, present to you. He said he was certain I was a man of birth, because I had small ears, curling hair, and little white hands, and expressed himself pleased with my appearance and garb. He told me to consider him as a father whilst I was in Turkey, and said he looked on me as his son. Indeed, he treated me like a child, sending me almonds and sugared sherbet, fruit and sweetmeats, twenty times a day. He begged me to visit him often, and at night, when he was at leisure. I then, after coffee and pipes, retired for the first time. I saw him thrice afterwards. It is singular that the Turks, who have no hereditary dignities, and few great families, except the Sultans, pay so much respect to birth; for I found my pedigree more regarded than my title.

His highness is sixty years old, very fat, and not tall,

2 William Martin Leake, later the author of topographical works.

but with a fine face, light blue eyes, and a white beard; his manner is very kind, and at the same time he possesses that dignity which I find universal amongst the Turks. He has the appearance of anything but his real character, for he is a remorseless tyrant, guilty of the most horrible cruelties, very brave, and so good a general that they call him the Mahometan Buonaparte. Napoleon has twice offered to make him King of Epirus, but he prefers the English interest, and abhors the French, as he himself told me. He is of so much consequence, that he is much courted by both, the Albanians being the most warlike subjects of the Sultan, though Ali is only nominally dependent on the Porte; he has been a mighty warrior, but is as barbarous as he is successful, roasting rebels, etc., etc. Buonaparte sent him a snuff-box with his picture. He said the snuff-box was very well, but the picture he could excuse, as he neither liked it nor the original. His ideas of judging of a man's birth from ears, hands, etc., were curious enough. To me he was, indeed, a father, giving me letters, guards, and every possible accommodation. Our next conversations were of war and travelling, politics, and England. He called my Albanian soldier, who attends me, and told him to protect me at all hazard; his name is Viscillie, and like all the Albanians, he is brave, rigidly honest, and faithful; but they are cruel, though not treacherous, and have several vices but no meannesses. They are, perhaps, the most beautiful race, in point of countenance, in the world; their women are sometimes handsome also, but they are treated like slaves, *beaten*, and, in short, complete beasts of burden; they plough, dig, and sow. I found them carrying wood, and actually repairing the highways. The men are all soldiers, and war and the chase their sole occupations. The women are the labourers, which after all is no great hardship in so delightful a climate. Yesterday, the 11th of November, I bathed in the sea; to-day is so hot that I am writing in a shady room of the English consul's, with three doors wide open, no fire, or even *fireplace,* in the house, except for culinary purposes.

Today I saw the remains of the town of Actium, near which Antony lost the world, in a small bay, where two frigates could hardly manœuvre: a broken wall is the sole remnant. On another part of the gulf stand the ruins of Nicopolis, built by Augustus in honour of his victory. Last night I was at a Greek marriage; but this and a thousand other things more I have neither time nor *space* to describe.

I am going to-morrow, with a guard of fifty men, to Patras in the Morea, and thence to Athens, where I shall winter. Two days ago I was nearly lost in a Turkish ship of war, owing to the ignorance of the captain and crew, though the storm was not violent. Fletcher yelled after his wife, the Greeks called on all the saints, the Mussulmans on Alla; the captain burst into tears and ran below deck, telling us to call on God; the sails were split, the main-yard shivered, the wind blowing fresh, the night setting in, and all our chance was to make Corfu, which is in possession of the French, or (as Fletcher pathetically termed it) 'a watery grave'. I did what I could to console Fletcher, but finding him incorrigible, wrapped myself up in my Albanian capote (an immense cloak), and lay down on deck to wait the worst. I have learnt to philosophise in my travels; and if I had not, complaint was useless. Luckily the wind abated and only drove us on the coast of Suli, on the main land, where we landed, and proceeded by the help of the natives, to Prevesa again; but I shall not trust Turkish sailors in future, though the Pacha had ordered one of his own galliots to take me to Patras. I am therefore going as far as Missolonghi by land, and there have only to cross a small gulf to get to Patras.

Fletcher's next epistle will be full of marvels. We were one night lost for nine hours in the mountains in a thunderstorm, and since nearly wrecked. In both cases Fletcher was sorely bewildered, from apprehensions of famine and banditti in the first, and drowning in the second instance. His eyes were a little hurt by the lightning, or crying (I don't know which), but are now recovered. When you write address to me at Mr. Strané's, English consul, Patras, Morea.

I could tell you I know not how many incidents that I think would amuse you, but they crowd on my mind as much as they would swell my paper, and I can neither arrange them in the one, nor put them down on the other, except in the greatest confusion. I like the Albanians much; they are not all Turks; some tribes are Christians. But their religion makes little difference in their manner or conduct. They are esteemed the best troops in the Turkish service. I lived on my route, two days at once, and three days again, in a barrack at Salora, and never found soldiers so tolerable, though I have been in the garrisons of Gibraltar and Malta, and seen Spanish, French, Sicilian, and British troops in abundance. I have had nothing stolen, and was always welcome to their provision and milk. Not a week ago an Albanian chief, (every village has its chief, who is called Primate,) after helping us out of the Turkish galley in her distress, feeding us, and lodging my suite, consisting of Fletcher, a Greek, two Athenians, a Greek priest, and my companion, Mr. Hobhouse, refused any compensation but a written paper stating that I was well received; and when I pressed him to accept a few sequins, 'No,' he replied; 'I wish you to love me, not to pay me'. These are his words.

It is astonishing how far money goes in this country. While I was in the capital I had nothing to pay by the vizier's order; but since, though I have generally had sixteen horses, and generally six or seven men, the expense has not been *half* as much as staying only three weeks in Malta, though Sir A. Ball,[3] the governor, gave me a house for nothing, and I had only *one servant*. By the by, I expect Hanson to remit regularly; for I am not about to stay in this province for ever. Let him write to me at Mr. Strané's, English consul, Patras. The fact is, the fertility of the plains is wonderful, and specie is scarce, which makes this remarkable cheapness. I am going to Athens, to study modern Greek, which differs much from the ancient, though radically similar. I have no desire to return to England, nor shall I, unless compelled by absolute want, and Hanson's neglect; but

[3] Rear-Admiral Sir Alexander John Ball.

I shall not enter into Asia for a year or two, as I have much to see in Greece, and I may perhaps cross into Africa, at least the Egyptian part. Fletcher, like all Englishmen, is very much dissatisfied, though a little reconciled to the Turks by a present of eighty piastres from the vizier, which, if you consider every thing, and the value of specie here, is nearly worth ten guineas English. He has suffered nothing but from cold, heat, and vermin, which those who lie in cottages and cross mountains in a cold country must undergo, and of which I have equally partaken with himself; but he is not valiant, and is afraid of robbers and tempests. I have no one to be remembered to in England, and wish to hear nothing from it, but that you are well, and a letter or two on business from Hanson, whom you may tell to write. I will write when I can, and beg you to believe me,

Your affectionate son,
BYRON

P.S.—I have some very 'magnifiques' Albanian dresses, the only expensive articles in this country. They cost fifty guineas each, and have so much gold, they would cost in England two hundred.

I have been introduced to Hussein Bey, and Mahmout Pacha, both little boys, grandchildren of Ali, at Yanina; they are totally unlike our lads, have painted complexions like rouged dowagers, large black eyes, and features perfectly regular. They are the prettiest little animals I ever saw, and are broken into the court ceremonies already. The Turkish salute is a slight inclination of the head, with the hand on the breast; intimates always kiss. Mahmout is ten years old, and hopes to see me again; we are friends without understanding each other, like many other folks, though from a different cause. He has given me a letter to his father in the Morea, to whom I have also letters from Ali Pacha.

TO THOMAS MOORE

Venice, December 24, 1816

... My flame (my *Donna* whom I spoke of in my former epistle, my Marianna) is still my Marianna, and I her—what she pleases. She is by far the prettiest woman I have seen here, and the most lovable I have met with any where—as well as one of the most singular. I believe I told you the rise and progress of our *liaison* in my former letter. Lest that should not have reached you, I will merely repeat, that she is a Venetian, two-and-twenty years old, married to a merchant well to do in the world, and that she has great black oriental eyes, and all the qualities which her eyes promise. Whether being in love with her has steeled me or not, I do not know; but I have not seen many other women who seem pretty. The nobility, in particular, are a sad-looking race—the gentry rather better. And now, what art *thou* doing?

> What are you doing now,
>   Oh Thomas Moore?
> What are you doing now,
>   Oh Thomas Moore?
>
> Sighing or suing now,
> Rhyming or wooing now,
> Billing or cooing now,
>   Which, Thomas Moore?

Are you not near the Luddites?[4] By the Lord! if there's a row, but I'll be among ye! How go on the weavers—

---

[4] Named after Ned Ludd, a village boy who began the practice of smashing machinery.

the breakers of frames—the Lutherans of politics—the reformers?

> As the Liberty lads o'er the sea
> Bought their freedom, and cheaply, with blood,
> So we, boys, we
> Will *die* fighting, or *live* free,
> And down with all kings but King Ludd!
>
> When the web that we weave is complete,
> And the shuttle exchanged for the sword,
> We will fling the winding-sheet
> O'er the despot at our feet
> And die it deep in the gore he has pour'd.
>
> Though black as his heart its hue,
> Since his veins are corrupted to mud,
> Yet this is the dew
> Which the tree shall renew
> Of Liberty, planted by Ludd!

There's an amiable *chanson* for you—all impromptu. I have written it principally to shock your neighbour[5] who is all clergy and loyalty—mirth and innocence—milk and water.

> But the Carnival's coming,
> Oh Thomas Moore,
> The Carnival's coming,
> Oh Thomas Moore,
> Masking and mumming,
> Fifing and drumming,
> Guitarring and strumming,
> Oh Thomas Moore.

[5] Perhaps Francis Hodgson, who on 18 July had been appointed to the living of Bakewell, Derbyshire.

The other night I saw a new play,—and the author. The subject was the sacrifice of Isaac. The play succeeded, and they called for the author—according to continental custom—and he presented himself, a noble Venetian, Mali—or Malapiero, by name. Mala was his name and *pessima* his production,—at least, I thought so; and I ought to know, having read more or less of five hundred Drury Lane offerings, during my coadjutorship with the sub-and-super Committee.

When does your Poem of Poems come out? I hear that the *E[dinburgh] R[eview]* has cut up Coleridge's *Christabel,* and declared against me for praising it.[6] I praised it, firstly, because I thought well of it; secondly, because Coleridge was in great distress, and after doing what little I could for him in essentials, I thought that the public avowal of my good opinion might help him further, at least with the booksellers. I am very sorry that J[effrey] has attacked him, because, poor fellow, it will hurt him in mind and pocket. As for me, he's welcome—I shall never think less of J[effrey] for anything he may say against me or mine in future.

I suppose Murray has sent you, or will send (for I do not know whether they are out or no) the poem, or poesies, of mine, of last summer. By the mass! they're sublime—*Ganion Coheriza*[7]—gainsay who dares! Pray, let me hear from you, and of you, and, at least, let me know that you have received these three letters. Direct right *here, poste restante.*

Ever and ever, etc.

6 He had called it "a wild and singularly original and beautiful poem."
7 *Chandeon co heirogha,* the motto of the Macdonalds of Clanranald.

P.S.—I heard the other day of a pretty trick of a book-seller,[8] who has published some damned nonsense, swearing the bastards to me, and saying he gave me five hundred guineas for them. He lies—I never wrote such stuff, never saw the poems, nor the publisher of them, in my life, nor had any communication, directly or indirectly, with the fellow. Pray say as much for me, if need be. I have written to Murray, to make him contradict the imposter.

[8] James Johnston.

TO JOHN MURRAY
Venice, May 15, 1819

. . . The story of Shelley's agitation is true. I can't tell what seized him, for he don't want courage. He was once with me in a gale of Wind, in a small boat, right under the rocks between Meillerie and St. Gingo. We were five in the boat—a servant, two boatmen, and ourselves. The sail was mismanaged, and the boat was filling fast. He can't swim. I stripped off my coat—made him strip off his and take hold of an oar, telling him that I thought (being myself an expert swimmer) I could save him, if he would not struggle when I took hold of him —unless we got smashed against the rocks, which were high and sharp, with an awkward surf on them at that minute. We were then about a hundred yards from shore, and the boat in peril. He answered me with the greatest coolness, that 'he had no notion of being saved, and that I would have enough to do to save myself, and begged not to trouble me.' Luckily, the boat righted, and, baling, we got round a point into St. Gingo, where the inhabitants came down and embraced the boatmen on their escape, the Wind having been high enough to tear up some huge trees from the Alps above us, as we saw next day.

TO JOHN MURRAY

Ravenna, June 29, 1819

. . . In the summer of 1817, Hobhouse and myself were
sauntering on horseback along the Brenta one evening,
when, amongst a group of peasants, we remarked two
girls as the prettiest we had seen for some time. About
this period, there had been great distress in the country,
and I had a little relieved some of the people. Generos-
ity makes a great figure at very little cost in Venetian
livres, and mine had probably been exaggerated—as an
Englishman's. Whether they remarked us looking at
them or no, I know not; but one of them called out to
me in Venetian, 'Why do not you, who relieve others,
think of us also?' I turned round and answered her—
'*Cara, tu sei troppo bella e giovane per aver' bisogno
del' soccorso mio*'. She answered, 'If you saw my hut and
my food, you would not say so'. All this passed half jest-
ingly, and I saw no more of her for some days.

A few evenings after, we met with these two girls
again, and they addressed us more seriously, assuring us
of the truth of their statement. They were cousins; Margarita married, the other single. As I doubted still of the
circumstances, I took the business up in a different light,
and made an appointment with them for the next evening. Hobhouse had taken a fancy to the single lady,
who was much shorter in stature, but a very pretty girl
also. They came attended by a third woman, who was
cursedly in the way, and Hobhouse's charmer took
fright (I don't mean at Hobhouse, but at not being mar-

ried—for here no woman will do anything under adultery), and flew off; and mine made some bother—at the propositions, and wished to consider of them. I told her, 'if you really are in want, I will relieve you without any conditions whatever, and you may make love with me or no just as you please—*that* shall make no difference; but if you are not in absolute necessity, this is naturally a rendezvous, and I presumed that you understood this when you made the appointment'. She said that she had no objection to make love with me, as she was married, and all married women did it; but that her husband [a baker] was somewhat ferocious, and would do her a mischief. In short, in a few evenings we arranged our affairs, and for two years, in the course of which I had more women than I can count or recount, she was the only one who preserved over me an ascendancy which was often disputed, and never impaired. As she herself used to say publicly, 'It don't matter, he may have five hundred; but he will always come back to me.'

The reasons of this were, firstly, her person—very dark, tall, the Venetian face, very fine black eyes—and certain other qualities which need not be mentioned. She was two-and-twenty years old, and, never having had children, had not spoilt her figure ********She was, besides, a thorough Venetian in dialect, in her thoughts, in her countenance, in every thing, with all their naïveté and Pantaloon humour. Besides, she could neither read nor write, and could not plague me with letters,—except twice that she paid sixpence to a public scribe, under the piazza, to make a letter for her, upon some occasion, when I was ill and could not see her. In other respects she was somewhat fierce and *prepotente,* that is, over-bearing, and used to walk in whenever it suited her, with no very great regard to time, place, nor persons; and if she found any women in her way, she knocked them down.

When I first knew her, I was in *relazione (liaison)* with la Signora Segati, who was silly enough one evening at Dolo, accompanied by some of her female friends, to threaten her; for the Gossips of the Villeggiatura had already found out, by the neighing of my horse one evening, that I used to 'ride late in the night' to meet the Fornarina. Margarita threw back her veil *(fazziolo),* and replied in very explicit Venetian, '*You* are *not* his *wife: I* am *not* his *wife: you* are his *Donna,* and *I* am his *Donna: your* husband is a cuckold, and *mine* is another. For the rest, what *right* have you to re-proach me? if he prefers what is mine to what is yours, is it my fault? if you wish to secure him, tie him to your petticoat-string; but do not think to speak to me with-out a reply, because you happen to be richer than I am.' Having delivered this pretty piece of eloquence (which I translate as it was related to me by a bye-stander), she went on her way, leaving a numerous audience with Madame Segati, to ponder at her leisure on the dialogue between them.

When I came to Venice for the Winter, she followed. I never had any regular *liaison* with her, but whenever she came I never allowed any other connection to inter-fere with her; and as she found herself out to be a fa-vourite, she came pretty often. But she had inordinate Self-love, and was not tolerant of other women, except of the Segati, who was, as she said, my regular *Amica,* so that, I being at that time somewhat promiscuous, there was great confusion and demolition of head-dresses and handkerchiefs; and sometimes my servants, in 'redding the fray'[9] between her and other feminine persons, received more knocks than acknowledgements for their peaceful endeavours. At the *Cavalchina,* the masqued ball on the last night of the Carnival, where all the World goes, she snatched off the mask of Madame Contarini, a lady noble by birth, and decent in conduct, for no other reason, but because she happened to be leaning on my arm. You may suppose what a cursed noise this made; but this is only one of her pranks.

At last she quarrelled with her husband, and one evening ran away to my house. I told her this would not do: she said she would lie in the street, but not go back to him; that he beat her (the gentle tigress), spent her money, and scandalously neglected his Oven. As it was Midnight I let her stay, and next day there was no moving her at all. Her husband came, roaring and crying, and entreating her to come back:—*not* she! He then applied to the Police, and they applied to me: I told them and her husband to *take* her; I did not want her; she had come, and I could not fling her out of the window; but they might conduct her through that or the door if they chose it. She went before the Commissary, but was obliged to return with that *becco ettico* ('consumptive cuckold'), as she called the poor man, who has a Ptisick. In a few days she ran away again. After a precious piece

[9] Cf. *Old Mortality,* chap. iv.

of work, she fixed herself in my house, really and truly without my consent, but, owing to my indolence, and not being able to keep my countenance; for if I began in a rage, she always finished by making me laugh with some Venetian pantaloonery or another; and the Gipsy knew this well enough, as well as her other powers of persuasion, and exerted them with the usual tact and success of all She-things—high and low, they are all alike for that.

Madame Benzone also took her under her protection, and then her head turned. She was always in extremes, either crying or laughing; and so fierce when angered, that she was the terror of men, women, and children— for she had the strength of an Amazon, with the temper of Medea. She was a fine animal, but quite untameable. *I* was the only person that could at all keep her in any order, and when she saw me really angry (which they tell me is rather a savage sight), she subsided. But she had a thousand fooleries: in her *fazziolo,* the dress of the lower orders, she looked beautiful; but, alas! she longed for a hat and feathers, and all I could say or do (and I said much) could not prevent this travestie. I put the first into the fire; but I got tired of burning them, before she did of buying them, so that she made herself a figure—for they did not at all become her.

Then she would have her gowns with a *tail*—like a lady, forsooth: nothing would serve her but '*l'abito colla coua,*' or *cua* (that is the Venetian for '*la Coda,*' the tail or train,) and as her cursed pronunciation of the word made me laugh, there was an end of all contro- versy, and she dragged this diabolical tail after her every where.

In the mean time, she beat the women and stopped my letters. I found her one day pondering over one: she used to try to find out by their shape whether they were feminine or no; and she used to lament her ignorance, and actually studied her Alphabet, on purpose (as she declared) to open all letters addressed to me and read their contents.

I must not omit to do justice to her housekeeping qualities: after she came into my house as *donna di governo,* the expences were reduced to less than half, and every body did their duty better—the apartments were kept in order, and every thing and every body else, except herself.

That she had sufficient regard for me in her wild way, I had many reasons to believe. I will mention one. In the autumn, one day, going to the Lido, with my Gondoliers, we were over-taken by a heavy squall, and the Gondola put in peril—hats blown away, boat filling, oar lost, tumbling sea, thunder, rain in torrents, night coming, and wind increasing. On our return, after a tight struggle, I found her on the open steps of the Mocenigo palace, on the Grand Canal, with her great black eyes flashing through her tears, and the long dark hair, which was streaming drenched with rain over her brows and breast. She was perfectly exposed to the storm; and the wind blowing her hair and dress about her tall thin figure, and the lightning flashing round her, with the waves rolling at her feet, made her look like Medea alighted from her chariot, or the Sibyl of the tempest that was rolling around her, the only living thing within hail at that moment except ourselves. On seeing me safe, she did not wait to greet me, as might be expected, but calling out to me—'*Ah! can' della Madonna, xe esto il tempo per andar' al' Lido?*' (Ah! Dog of the Virgin, is this a time to go to Lido?') ran into the house, and solaced herself with scolding the boatmen for not foreseeing the '*temporale.*' I was told by the servants that she had only been prevented from coming in a boat to look after me, by the refusal of all the Gondoliers of the Canal to put out into the harbour in such a moment: and that then she sate down on the steps in all the thickest of the Squall, and would neither be removed or comforted. Her joy at seeing me again was moderately mixed with ferocity, and gave me the idea of a tigress over her recovered Cubs.

But her reign drew near a close. She became quite ungovernable some months after; and a concurrence of complaints, some true, and many false—'a favourite has no friend'[10]—determined me to part with her. . . .

[10] Gray, "*Ode on the Death of a Favourite Cat.*"

TO THE HON DOUGLAS KINNAIRD
Venice, April 24th, 1819

. . . I have fallen in love, within the last month, with a Romagnuola Countess from Ravenna, the spouse of a year of Count Guiccioli, who is sixty—the girl twenty.

She is as fair as sunrise, and warm as noon, but she is young, and was not content with what she had done, unless it was to be turned to the advantage of the public, and so she made an éclat, which rather astonished even the Venetians, and electrified the Conversazioni of the Benzona, the Albrizzi, and the Michelli, and made her husband look embarrassed.

They have been gone back to Ravenna some time, but they return in the winter. She is the queerest woman I ever met with, for in general they cost one something one way or other, whereas by an odd combination of circumstances, I have proved an expense to HER, which is not *my* custom, but an accident; however it don't matter.

She is a sort of Italian Caroline Lamb, except that she is much prettier, and not so savage. But she has the same red-hot head, the same noble disdain of public opinion, with the superstructure of all that Italy can add to such natural dispositions.

She is also of the Ravenna noblesse, educated in a convent, sacrificed to wealth, filial duty, and all that.

I am damnably in love, but they are gone, for many months—and nothing but hope keeps me alive *seriously*.

Yours ever, B.

INDEX OF TITLES

INDEX OF FIRST LINES

ABOUT HORACE GREGORY

Horace Gregory was born in Milwaukee, Wisconsin. He received his formal education at the Milwaukee School of Fine Arts, the German-English Academy, and the University of Wisconsin. His early preoccupation with Latin verse resulted in three volumes of translation: *The Poems of Catullus, Ovid's Metamorphoses,* and *Love Poems of Ovid.* From 1934 until 1960 Mr. Gregory taught classical literature and modern poetry at Sarah Lawrence College.

Besides seven volumes of his own poetry, Mr. Gregory has written a study of the works of D. H. Lawrence, critical biographies of Amy Lowell and James McNeill Whistler, and a study of Dorothy Richardson's *Pilgrimage.* In 1942 his *Poems, 1930–1940* won the Russell Loines award, and in 1965 his *Collected Poems* received the 1963–64 Bollingen prize. He is a member of the National Institute of Arts and Letters and a recipient of an Academy of American Poets Fellowship award.

Mr. Gregory and his wife, the poet Marya Zaturenska, live in Rockland County, New York.

ABOUT THE ILLUSTRATOR

Virgil Burnett is an artist, illustrator, and designer for the theater. His drawings have been exhibited in Paris and in New York and other American cities. He is an associate professor in the Art Department of the University of Chicago.

Mr. Burnett received his bachelor's degree from Columbia University and his master's degree in art history from the University of California. He has studied at the University of Paris and worked as an assistant to a French publisher.

Mr. Burnett divides his time between an apartment in Chicago and a house in France. He is married and has two daughters.